The Edgier Waters

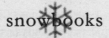

snowbooks

PUBLISHED BY SNOWBOOKS 2006

SPECIAL PROMOTIONAL EDITION

Introduction © 2006 Michael Bracewell
Preface © 2006 A. Stevens
For the copyright on individual pieces see pages 289-291

Proudly published in Great Britain by
Snowbooks Ltd.
120 Pentonville Road
London N1 9JN
www.snowbooks.com

A CIP catalogue record for this book
is available from the British Library

ISBN 1-905-00553-9
ISBN-13 978-1-905-0055-36

The Edgier Waters

5 YEARS OF 3:AM MAGAZINE

Edited by A. Stevens

"3:AM... for a dip into the edgier waters of literature"
The Guardian

CONTENTS

FOREWORD

Michael Bracewell

Tirelessly enquiring and determinedly eclectic, the
3:AM literary magazine has always pioneered a reading of contemporary international fiction which confounds any single mission statement. In this 3:AM
has become a literary and cultural venue which defies
both fashionability and market forces—no mean
achievement during an era which is often seen to be
enslaved to precisely those demands.

In many ways, much of the work which has been
published or discussed by 3:AM has been produced
from a position which is either oppositional, sepa-
ratist, or, dare one say it, a postmodern reclamation
of the historic values of the counterculture. (As one
might, for instance, wonder what the counterculture
might comprise in the opening years of the twenty
first century.) And as such, it is maybe a worthwhile,
not too strenuous exercise, to take a glance at the

culture out of which or against many of the writers who have contributed to 3:AM have taken their bearings.

Back in the 1980s, the sudden commercial success of the so-called 'Brat Pack' of American literary fiction—notably, Bret Easton Ellis, Jay McInerney and Tama Janowitz—alerted the funky end of publishing to the idea that there might be a vast new readership for a new kind of fiction.

McInerney *et al* were writing about a specific evolutionary phase of white, bourgeois American dysfunctionalism. Indeed, McInerney's novel *Story of My Life*, published in the UK by Bloomsbury in 1988, began (if I remember rightly) with the dinner party-stopping line: "Like, like I don't need this shit..." The territory being covered was that of the drug-sodden, prematurely aged, shopped-to-death society of over-privileged, over-indulged young Americans—a world, in fact, already planted with the reasonably imperial and immoveable flags of Andy Warhol and Tom Wolfe.

But the books were filled with visceral energy and tack-spitting irony; they sold well, and their authors comprised a distinctly media-friendly cast of Armani besuited subjects. They came to represent a postmodern update of the Fitzgeraldian view of a privileged younger generation engaged on a perilous, vertiginous, morally compromising spree—with the jazz and cocktails of Fitzgerald's Yale graduates and bobbed-haired popular daughters being replaced with the grunge and cocaine of wealthy trustafarians and whacked-out suburban libertines.

The success of the Brat Pack coincided, however, with an equally forceful conflation of other cultural directives. In the UK, earlier in the 1980s, the arrival from New York of Kathy Acker—off the back of her commercially successful collection for Picador, *Blood and Guts In High School + Two*—had introduced younger British writers (and publishers) to the idea that there could possibly be a connection between the people who bought interesting records (this was still a largely pre-CD era, amazingly) and the people who bought interesting books. Acker presented herself as part rebel bohemian avant-gardiste, part NYC downtown punk, and part venerable literary grande dame. Stylistically and thematically her work—clever, infuriating, aggressive, neurotic, at times poetic, determinedly confrontational—was the direct opposite to that of the Brat-packers.

But Acker—unlike, for instance, a profoundly literary contemporary such as her fellow avant-gardiste New Yorker Lynne Tillmann—was both of the literary world and outside it. She fitted and she didn't, for the very reason that she wanted to risk taking her writing, its style and subject, to places which might well be perceived to lack academic or literary respectability. All of which she did with a kind of reckless give-a-shit determination to be contrary—even when the celebrity and applause with which her work had first been greeted had long since died down.

It was in the identification of a position between literature and the weird, vexed, culturally elastic legacy of post-punk music and 'style' culture which would make Acker, in many ways, a precursing figure to the literary and cultural territory which 3:AM magazine would subsequently come to explore. The identification—as the contents of this selection of writings reveal—of a post-modern literature which could be every bit as nihilistic and ironic as the world described by the Brat Packers, but which also recognized, as if by reflex, that there had to be a world, many worlds even, beyond irony and nihilism.

The second literary phenomenon to occur towards the end of the 1980s would be the sudden emergence of a largely apolitical school of social realism—its subject matter, whether hard-cased in mischief-making postmodern cleverness or not, being very much the new urban underground (if an underground could still exist) of the so-called chemical generation. In the UK, the success of the new generation of Celtic writers (their works in many ways linked to the vision and writings of James Kelman) would foreground a literature which was deeply vernacular, phonetic, at times bleak and at times game-playing. Above all, it raised questions relating to cultural and artistic authenticity—what might comprise a literature made during a time of rampant cultural materialism, and the postmodern condition in which quotation appeared to have replaced authorship?

And these, too, would be some of the issues that

3:AM—never taking itself too seriously, however—might aim to address. They bring to mind the challenge laid down by Ezra Pound, towards the end of his epic *Cantos*—"I have brought the great ball of crystal; Who can lift it?" Which is a good question to roll around the mind, on days like these.

PREFACE

A. Stevens

The inspiration for this collection of prose and essays came from a copy of Maurice Girodias' *The Best of Olympia* I discovered in the Notting Hill Book Exchange, in the rack set aside for 'cult' fiction that heaves under the weight of Ballard, Selby Jr and dependency culture novels. The dog-eared copy was inscribed 'To John, from Babs' (you can inscribe your own to this copy, if you want) and in it Girodias wrote of the challenges facing the small press editor of his day, of printing errors, petty feuds among editors and precious writers making unreasonable demands on his time. In an era of diminished progress not much has changed; just substitute printing for webmastering and you get the idea. Even so, the fact that 3:AM has just completed its fifth year of existence gives a more plausible air to putting together this anthology.

Publishing a literary journal on the internet does create more possibilities for interaction between contributors, friends and foes than either the Grub Street era or the post-war scenes permitted. When we started five years ago, there were a clutch of online literary concerns emerging from the post-dot.com boom. There are now literally thousands. 3:AM is devoid of a mission statement and for that reason it works—for us anyhow. We have been told that 3:AM's appeal to its readers lies in its coverage of 'cult' literature. To some extent, the labels 'cult' and 'transgressive' might be said not to apply as we solely focus on what is of interest to us and if others share that interest then all the better. We just don't have to abide by the rules of market forces in that regard, the ones that force even the most august or highbrow of organs to cover mundane publishing phenomena. For us, the likes of Salman Rushdie and Julian Barnes are of zero interest – but they might yet be (though it's doubtful). This aesthetic without an ethos sees New Puritans sit alongside the likes of Billy Childish and Steve Aylett, the Underground Literary Alliance alongside Paul Auster, Stuckists and Britart apologists on the same page also. We feel no pressure to talk about bankable young authors, though we can't pretend not to notice when the broadsheets talk about us: the title of the book you're holding in your hands is testimony to that.

We've always been fascinated by the interplay between literature and music and in this volume there are contributions by writers who also double up as musicians (or vice versa): Billy Childish, Mike Watt and Thurston Moore for starters. The contributors hail from Britain, France or America, or in several cases Europe via America (and Japan even). The magazine has always been about literature in its global context; the internet alone saw to that. Like many before it, it remains based in France (via a US server) and is also edited from Britain and the US.

For all this, it remains the case that we're concerned with the kind of authors Elizabeth Young would be writing about if she was still with us. In his foreword, Michael Bracewell invokes Kathy Acker to the same end. Authors writing about authors always makes for good copy. Bruce Benderson's piece here forms an appreciation of the "dick-chasing literature" of Burroughs et al, lamenting its demise today due to the gradual acceptance of gay sex in mainstream culture.

It works both ways, of course. Alexander Trocchi was also thinking about "white calves in black ski pants" in the existentialist circles of Paris and it goes on. Only last month we published an interview with one young American writer from Prague who claimed that "writers have unique opportunities to have sex with women who wear glasses".

Girodias lives on. So do we.

ENOUGH RIBENA TO INCARNADINE THE MULTITUDINOUS SEAS

Andrew Gallix

Originally Published: 2000

Once upon a time my sister baked a battalion of gingerbread men who seemed destined for doughy, doughty deeds so gallant were they. I simply couldn't bring myself to eat them; had neither the heart nor the stomach to do so. A moratorium was declared by sisterly decree and the spice boys remained in battle formation on the kitchen table pending mum's final verdict. You could smell the sensuous, exotic aroma from my bedroom, even behind closed door.

That night, I had this vivid dream in which the ithyphallic gingerbread men rose from the baking tray Galatea-fashion. Still under the influence of the self-raising flour, they legged it upstairs to gang-bang the Play-Doh model of the Girl Next Door I had lovingly sculpted and kept secretly beside my comics and sensible shoes.

Breakfast, the morning after, was a truly religious experience. I binged ravenously on the horny homunculi, tearing away at their limbs, biting off their heads with sheer abandon, and washing them down with enough glasses of Ribena to incarnadine the multitudinous seas.

EROS ESSAY

Tim Parks

Originally Published: 2000

If Brahma is a more endearing creator than Jehovah it is because he wasn't pleased with what he had made. The great god found the world dull and dusty. Death was the answer, suggested Shiva. Living forever, people were bored. A time-limit would galvanise, give dignity. But in that case some way of replacing the population would have to be found. Brahma brought together a few trusted fellows and explained what was required. The pleasure took them by surprise. What was that for? To put a fresh shine on the world, they were told. Otherwise it might get dusty again...

I'm always taken aback when people talk about the eroticism of food and drink, of sunbathing and massage. This is mere sensuality. Or avoiding the issue. No experience even remotely compares with true eros, with long and lavish love-making. It is perfectly understandable that people should imagine its having

3

been tacked on to creation afterwards, so extravagant is the pleasure it brings, so far beyond what is necessary. Never does the world seem so freshly painted, so brightly enamelled, so new, for heaven's sake, as after the best sex. But, alas, depending on where you're up to in life, it may be full of new complications too. A lesser authority than Brahma's would have issued a health-warning.

Over billiards and beer a friend is explaining why he is leaving his wife and two children. He's playing with unusual speed and precision. His eyes are brighter than the beer could account for. 'And the girl is twenty-three,' he explains. French. So intelligent. 'Intelligently pert breasts?' I enquire, 'Perceptively warm thighs?' He laughs. He is deliriously proud, confused, unhappy. 'I feel I was never really in love with my wife,' he says.

Eroticism paints out the past. In this sense it is the most potent myth-making and myth-destroying power we have. How those first encounters are told and re-told, cherished and savoured over and over again. How solid and irreplaceable they begin to seem. I did this, you said that. When your hand first ... When your mouth ... Beneath all the structure of domestic economy, in-laws, even children, it is on this bedrock that marriage rests. But only once? Is it never to happen again? Suddenly solid ground is quicksand...

'As soon as I'm in the door, I feel suffocated. I married too young.' Thus Franco, potting the black. 'I never experienced real passion.' Before *la jeune-fille très intelligente*, he means. And is setting up the table again. He is smoking too this evening. I have never seen him smoke before. 'I feel I will die if I go home,' he says. I ask him if he wants more children. He doesn't. 'Perhaps it's all a terrible mistake,' he says, 'but at least I will have had this passion.' Should I tell him that when we first met years ago he had seemed very passionate about his wife? Who is nothing if not intelligent...

Women. Another Indian myth—sexist, if you wish to be offended—has it that when the gods became scared of a man, scared of his developing spiritual powers, they would send him a woman. Or alternatively they might send Indra to seduce his wife and make him jealous. In either case, the turbulent feelings would disperse the power he had accumulated. So Franco, whose expertise once took him round all the capitals of Europe, now finds his life in pieces. Lawyers, quarrels, returns, departures. Then more women too. For if marriage has a way of declining into dusty routine, myth-making likewise can lapse into tawdry chronicle. The third marriage, the fourth. Meantime, my billiards is improving.

Eroticism has this in common with an addictive drug: that there is a coercive element to its pleasure with which part of us is in complicity, and part not. Thus ever since time began men have been trying to enjoy eroticism without being destroyed by it. Societies, religions can be defined in the way they deal

5

with this conundrum. Polygamy, monogamy with repression, monogamy with affairs, monogamy with prostitutes, serial monogamy. Not to mention individual solutions of great ingenuity, or desperation: Victor Hugo with the door knocked through the wall of his office, to let in a girl each afternoon. Auden's flare for finding call-boys in every town. Picasso who simply refused when wife and mistress demanded he choose between them. Then there is always the hair-shirt of course. But perhaps the thing to remember when you wake up with a life full of fresh paint and tortuous complications is that eroticism wasn't invented for you, nor merely for the survival of the species perhaps, but for a divinity's entertainment. Nothing generates so many opportunities for titillation and schadenfreude as eroticism. Which is why it lies at the centre of so much narrative. How the gods thronged the balconies of heaven to see the consequences of Helen's betrayal! And your friends are watching too. Your antics have put the shine on many a late-night conversation.

On the borders between mythology and history, that wily survivor Odysseus was the first who learnt to trick the gods. And perhaps his smartest trick of all was that of lashing himself to the mast before the Sirens came in earshot. There are those of course who are happy to stand at the railings, even scan the horizon. Otherwise, choose your mast, find the ropes that suit you: sport, workaholism, celibacy with prayerbook and bell ... But the kindest and toughest ropes of all are probably to be found in some suburban semi-detached with rowdy children and a woman who never allows the dust to settle for too long

THE NEW BOHEMIANS

Utahna Faith

Originally Published: 2001

The light creeps into the edges of their night, their night that feels endless, timeless, like they'd like life to be. Vampire nights flying between New Orleans' Lower Decatur Street, Frenchman Street, the Hideout, the Spotted Cat, the Dragon's Den, The Abbey.

They will live forever, young and beautiful and excited and exciting. If only the dawn wouldn't come.

They are dizzy with decadence, with guitar notes or brush strokes or poetry, with Cosmos or bourbon or Chartreuse or Burgundy, each to his or her own. They are dancing and laughing and making plans they are forgetting to make time for. They are spilling out secrets like liquid from a top-heavy but beautiful martini glass onto the already sticky Abbey floor. They spill their secrets into one another's ears, in the drunken fest of trust and love and temporarily invulnerable vulnerability.

And then the light comes. The staunchest of them deny, hide. The slotted plastic curtains of the Abbey doorway fall. The light inside doesn't dim for night or brighten for daytime. One of the group, the one farthest gone, might pull out black-rimmed sunglasses; another might say, gently, baby, it's not that bright yet. Sweetie, no, we're inside.

And the dawn keeps coming. They ignore it, but still it comes.

City workers wash the streets. Sometimes the drinkers see the big, low, street-cleaning trucks inching by. More often they don't notice; they only look outside, marvelling at the lightness and the hour, as they deposit more quarters in the jukebox next to the door. They see that the street is wet, and each time it tricks them for a moment. Has it rained? They look at the sky, clear and lavender and growing lighter by the moment. Soon the sun will shine. They will wend their way home, helping one another. They may stagger or skip or meander. Sunglasses are *de rigueur*, now.

They pass the creamy buildings on Ursuline Street, antebellum structures milky in buttercup yellow, rosy brick, white-chocolate mint.

They duck into Croissant d'Or, black-clad and smoky among fresh morning joggers. The revellers lean against one another sleepily and order hot cocoa and croissants.

This is living. This is dying, slowly, as we each are from the moment we are born.

THE DEFIANT PROSE OF STEWART HOME

Richard Marshall

Originally Published: 2001

Stewart Home is out to cause trouble. The works of Pierre Bourdieu, especially *Distinction: A Social Critique Of The Judgement Of Taste*, alongside that of Marx and the European avant-garde, have given him the rhetorical and cultural capital to launch his assaults. His is a defiant pose from an explicitly Red London-English working-class position that aims to do serious damage to the chic aristocracy of culture. It wants to mess up those symbolic systems and power relations in which distinctions of taste become the basis for social judgement. His use of pornography, skinhead violence and extreme politics in his novels, journals and pranks challenge the powerful ruling bourgeois who organise their radicalism in the chic tasteful habitus of bouillabaisse, thinness, authenticity, angst, relativism and Salman Rushdie. Home can be seen as a contemporary working-class dissenter rooted in a tradition that requires intellectuals to reconstitute what it means to be a thinker. This is a radical, absurdist project in a time of cultural and economic globalisation. What he does is as offensive to the intelligentsia as a Pentecostal from the foothills of the Chautauqua Mountains at the dinner table of Bourdieu's 'Truly Classical' University Teacher of 'sobriety' and 'discretion'! But it would be wrong to see Home as a one-off, eccentric crank. We can hear his rude-boy voice in, for example, the seething London cabals of radical dissenters of the early nineteenth century which in turn links him to an old and important dissenting tradition.

In the 1830's, print worker Hetherington's *Poor Man's Guardian* had the motto 'Knowledge is power' and the heading "Published contrary to 'Law' to try the power of 'Might' against 'Right'." EP Thompson reports that Hetherington, in his opening address of *The Poor Man's Guardian* "… quoted clause by clause the laws he intended to defy… to excite hatred and contempt of the Government and Constitution of… this country, as BY LAW established… to vilify the ABUSES of religion… or any other acts whatsoever and despite the 'laws' or the will and pleasure of any tyrant or body of tyrants whatsoever, any thing herein-before, or any-where-else… to the contrary notwithstanding". A radical dissenting working-class voice was in those years a force to be reckoned with in literary circles. This should be understood not just in terms of the ideas about the working class, but in terms of the production of those ideas. The Chartist press, as Thompson reminds us, came at the point where the working class was "no longer in the making but already made. The point we must note is the degree to which the fight for press liberties was a central formative influence upon the shaping movement". The working class was in charge of the production and distribution of its own culture, as well as its consumption.

In presenting views that contested the authority of the ruling classes the hundreds of news vendors, hawkers and voluntary agents were constantly under threat from the law. Many were thrown into prison, flogged, put under police surveillance, chained and fettered. Being poor, the consequences of such persecution would often have terrible consequences for the individuals concerned. Thompson quotes Wickwar's "Second Trial Of William Hone" (1818) which cites the case of one "... Robert Swindels, confined in Chester castle, while his wife and baby died from neglect, and his remaining child was placed in the poorhouse". This world of the radicalised publishing working-class milieu is known well enough.

Something else to note about this world is the timidity, hypocrisy and commercial greed of literary 'star-turns' such as Southey, Poet Laureate, who turned against his radical youth to "seek an injunction against Sherwin for infringement of copyright." Sherwin, to the delight of radical England had resurrected "Watt Tyler", Southey's republican indiscretion. Hazlitt writes: "Is it not a little strange that while this gentleman is getting an injunction against himself as the author of Watt Tyler, he is recommending gagging bills against us, and thus making up by force for his deficiency in argument."

Another element of this culture is the use of ridicule. Hone, Cruikshank, Carlisle, Davidson, Benbow are examples of piss-takers, pranksters and jokers who used their slapstick rhetoric and parodic works to entertain, incite, educate and instruct a huge radicalised readership. As Thompson remarks 'This was the culture—with its eager disputations around the bookseller's stalls, in the taverns, workshops and coffee houses—which Shelley saluted in his 'Song to the Men of England' and within which the genius of Dickens matured".

English dissenting culture's cosmopolitan and multi-disciplinary roots are other defining features. The example of Hazlitt is instructive: Hazlitt's father was an Irish Unitarian from Co. Tipperary, a friend of Welsh Presbyterian Priestly and American Benjamin Franklin, supporter of the French Revolution and a man whose support for American rebels against the English Crown forced him to Ireland and after the American War Of Independence to the USA. As Paulin notes, "Intellectually, they [The Hazlitts] ... were the descendants of the Commonwealth men who briefly made England a republic in the middle of the seventeenth century... in a line of descent from Milton, Harrington, and Algernon Sidney". Hazlitt began as a philosopher and painter before becoming a brilliant essayist in his early thirties. He even wrote a novel. Paulin writes that "Hazlitt combined aesthetics with an implicit invocation of Whig political action—bold, turbulent, risk-taking, decisively intelligent." He was anything but a specialist and what Paulin reconnects us with is the idea of craft journalism and prose as being vital, vernacular, radicalised aesthetic forces equal to poetry and painting.

Attempts to discredit and repress this tradition of English culture have been all-pervasive and successful for much of the time. T.S. Eliot represents this hegemonic anti-dissenting, anti-republican, anti-vernacular vision of Englishness. The fetishised nature of Eliotic values within the current education debate, expertly dissected in B Marshall's *English Teachers, The Unofficial Guide*, reflects the dispute between Eliot's tradition of Monarchical, Anglo-Catholic, hierarchical culture and an engaged democracy. At one point Marshall says "Christopher Hitchens identifies as '... that strain of oratory, pamphleteering and prose that runs through Milton, Bunyan, Burns and Blake... what the common folk like to call the Liberty Tree. This stream as charted by EP Thompson and others often flows underground for long periods. In England it disappeared for a long time.'"

On a bad evening it's possible to imagine an England where the disappearance of the English working class from the production and readership of philosophy, art, novels and journalism is largely accepted and found acceptable by those journalists, novelists, fine artists and cultural critics who have noticed this situation and who have access to placing their work with publishers, galleries, newspapers and so on. The institutional base of all current art, journalism and fiction is not sympathetic to the idea of working-class culture, nor is there room for a working-class dissenting tradition to flourish and elaborate itself. The Eliotic cultural hegemony ensures that any democratic, egalitarian, militant cultural work is largely gagged. Something deadening and hopelessly hierarchical strangles the vernacular voices. All that remains are commodified careerists and deferential sybarites who play at being 'radical' but who are merely lap-dancers on Capitalism's' table. On a bad evening this doesn't seem so hard to imagine.

So out of this dystopian, totalitarian gloom only the excluded could possibly begin to make things better. For some, this is the definition of avant garde. If art is but a subset of writing, painting, reviewing, making crafts and is part of the trap rather than an escape route for the poor, then an assault on art itself is the heretical position to adopt. The logic of this is important: heresy works from within its own censure. Christ the rebel Jew; Luther the rebel Roman Catholic; Marx the rebel Hegelian.

It is out of that context that the most impressive single contemporary contribution to the production, control and consumption of art culture both about and for the English working class is found. Routing himself along a strictly anti-authoritarian, cosmopolitan (mainly European), multi-disciplinary and anti-careerist trajectory of journalism, installation art shows, videos, pamphlets, festivals, piss-takes, music gigs, stand-up routines, lectures, debates, CDs, experimental radio and novels, is found the London prole worker Stewart Home.

The dissenting tradition he lines up to work out of is original and twists received ideas about English working-class culture into something much more provocative, difficult and inspiring than is usually presented, even by those mining a dissenting tradition. He writes that "it is easy enough to perceive a tradition running from the Free Spirit through the writings of Winstanley, Coppe, Sade, Fourier, Lautreamont, William Morris, Alfred Jarry, and on into Futurism and Dada—then via Surrealism into Lettrism, the various Situationist movements, Fluxus, 'Mail Art', Punk Rock, Neoism and contemporary anarchist cults". He argues: "If the term 'art' took on its modern meaning in the eighteenth century, then any opposition to it must date from this period—or later. ... Art has taken over the function of religion, not simply as the ultimate—and ultimately unknowable—form of knowledge, but also as the legitimised form of male emotionality. The 'male' artist is treated as a 'genius' for expressing feelings that are 'traditionally' considered 'feminine'. 'He' constructs a world in which the male is heroicised by displaying 'female' traits; and the female is reduced to an incipid subordinate role. 'Bohemia' is colonised by bourgeois men—a few of whom are 'possessed' by genius, the majority of whom are 'eccentric'. Bourgeois wimmin whose behaviour resembles that of the 'male genius' are dismissed as being 'hysterical'—while proletarians of either sex who behave in such a manner are simply branded as 'mental'. Although its apologists claim 'art is a universal category', this simply isn't true. Every survey of attendances at art galleries and museums demonstrates that an 'appreciation' of 'art' is something restricted almost exclusively to individuals belonging to higher income groups".

The tradition he lists becomes explicable in terms of these heretical views. For Milton , read Coppe, for Kant, Sade, and so on. And the vernacular, no-nonsense style is part of the story. He'll cite *Distinction: A Social Critique Of The Judgement Of Taste* by Pierre Bourdieu just to show he's overqualified in making this observation. This is a working-class voice that is cosmopolitan, clever and intellectually alert. Anyone who works in a comprehensive school knows about this state secret.

This is a tradition he constructed in 1988, a year before Greil Marcus, the American cultural critic, published his *Lipstick Traces: a Secret History Of The Twentieth Century*, a book which covered much of the same ground. The difference between the two books is instructive. Not only did Home get there first but Home wrote a slimmer, more urgent and demystified outline than Marcus. Home's was an anti-establishment tract working without any institutional academic backing. Marcus refused to review it even though he was asked to. The secrecy in his title becomes ironical once you realise that Marcus conspired to keep it so until he was ready to reveal it. Whereas Marcus's book was out on a major American publishing house with good distribution and publicity organisation, Homes' slimmer, more brutalising text was first published by 'Aporia Press and Unpopular Books'. 'Nuff said! It was unable to muster the same institutional support. Marcus's review would have been welcome oxygen in a world where the good review is crucial to a book's life. It didn't happen.

Not only that, but whereas Marcus's book trembles with atmospherics , so that the experience is obscurantic, operatic and religious, Home goes at the avant-garde movements and groups with a fierce, defiant stylistic economy which allows no pity, no reverence. Marcus knows that what he's writing about is 'art' and obscure genius. Why else would he be bothering with it? Home knows that its more important than that. And nowhere near as important either. What Home is sure about is that each of the movements described soon disintegrated into 'art', or wanting to be 'art' and are put to one side as utterly finished and bankrupt. This no-nonsense approach can be gleaned from just reading the chapter headings. Each movement is given a chapter. We then move on. Mercilessly. From Cobra and the Lettrist Movement through to Class War, in seventeen chapters and less than a hundred pages.

Out of this Home walks from London suburban punk to President Of The Western World, Neoist,

Neoist renegade, Festival Of Plagiarism/Art Strike avatar, annalist and undertaker, anarchist spanker and fascist baiter. What makes Home interesting is the street-fighter quality of what he is doing, the urgency and vernacular muscle that structures and informs his moves. The thinking takes place on the hoof, moving restlessly like a method actor or boxer, jabbing and hooking away at some unfinished, unfinishable project: "While the contemporary avant-garde shares its precursor's desire to attack the institution of art, it also differs fundamentally from its classical predecessor. If Futurism, Dada and Surrealism wanted to integrate art and life, today's avant-garde wants to consign the former category to oblivion. This is the return at a higher level of Islamic-cum-Protestant iconoclasm. Whilst the classical avant-garde was ultimately Deist in its attitude towards art, its progeny has taken up a stance of intransigent atheism in its antagonistic relationship to the dominant culture."

Home is therefore found deadpan and rough in his scandalous handling of art, the artists and the academics and critics who perpetuate it: "What Duchamp and the artists who followed in his wake realised was that they lived in societies based on fraud, They set out to expose social hypocrisy and had a lot of fun while they were at it. In the 1950's it was the Italian artists who pulled the most outrageous stunts. Giuseppe Pinot-Gallizio ... Piero Manzoni canned his excrement and flogged it as 'Artist's Shit'... . In the sixties Andy Warhol found his own fame so tiresome that he once sent a lookalike to take his place on a lecture tour. During the seventies , English feminist Cosey Fanni Tutti managed to get paid twice for making her art works. She posed for pornographic magazines and then exhibited the published results as part of the Prostitution show at the prestigious Institute of Contemporary Arts...." His routines are serious provocations. The joke is in the response. Slick satire or cynicism is just part of the society he is attacking, posh boys showing off before they get their film, TV and book deals. *Disputations On Art, Anarchy and Assholism* by Stewart Home and "friends" (Sabotage Editions BM Senior, 1997), *Outtakes* (1998), *Analecta* (Sabotage Editions, 1996) are examples of his wind-up pranks. Iain Sinclair on the back of *Analecta* is quoted as thinking these works offer "A survey more accurate, on every level, than the fact-checked responses of telephone journalists."

Home writes all his prose like a journalist. It is urgent, to the present moment, has the momentum of deadlines and the cut and thrust zest of current argument. It also bristles with quotes and references, useful in pulling the wool over reader's eyes as well as making them sit up and sweat. (Although he writes in an essay that "My attitude to journalism has always been to follow my own interests and wait for people to approach—it always struck me as a waste of time to go out and undersell myself".) Reading this, we detect the tongue-in-cheek dig against the work ethic and a nod towards Idling, yet another twisting of the knife in the class war. You can hear the collective grinding of teeth and the dark mutterings—working class, shirking class more like!

Always understanding that class war cannot be separated from snobbery, and intellectual snobbery in the world of the arts is part of its structure, no accidental adjunct, Home mobilises the very texts usually used to codify and reinforce the attitudes he denounces. Clearly delighting in his role of provocateur, the idea of out theorising the theorists is yet another prank in the Home repertoire. The spontaneous violence of his style, its realised determination to avoid respectability, where "respectability" defines a finished middle class of an earlier age, brings to mind what an admiring Hazlitt had to say about Burke's prose, his political opponent.

Burke's *Reflections* were for Hazlitt full of flashy images, dirty tricks and inspired declamation; "I have tried half a dozen times to describe Burke's style without ever succeeding—its severe extravagance; its literal boldness; its matter-of-fact hyperboles; its running away with a subject, and from it at the same time—but there is no making it out, for there is no example of the same thing anywhere else. We have no common measure to refer to; and his qualities contradict even themselves." This list is a good description of the bewildering torso of Home's writing oeuvre rather than his style. Yet Home's deliberately unpolished, non-classical prose sometimes confounds with the object representing it the very ideas he seems to discourse. At other times he works through an elaborate, understated double-bluff whereby he uses the English Hegelian torture-prose of certain academic sociological and cultural critics in order to deconstruct the sluggish moronism of, say, Heideggerian or Debordian totalitarianism.

Home masters his materials without falling foul of style slavery. This crucial distinction between the poet and the prose writer is made by Hazlitt. Immediacy, suddenness and excitement are the thing, as Hazlitt writes in his essay "The Fight": "There was little cautious sparring, no half hits, no tapping and trifling, none of the petit maitreship of the art—they were almost all knock-down blows." Home aims to write with the same effect. He aims to wind up his readers, wants to imagine them reacting, gives them things that they have to grapple with. To write in a style that is punchy and unambiguous, he jumps about like a real voice, creates the urgent noise of the insolent street-wise wise-cracker, the throughput of the nabbed street blagger faced by the heavy fist of the plod.

His use of deceit and plagiarism is a light-hearted prank, a thrust against the fetish of originality and genius that he sees as being part of the structure of modern notions of art, especially perhaps in fiction writing that draws attention to the power of such ideas. Similarly, the use of shared names, such as Karen Elliot, Luther Blissett, Monty Cantsin are equally prankster routines designed to reveal modern art's need for the genius. The unsettling of these ideas—of drawing attention to the fact that 'Art' is structured around concepts of genius, of originality, of creativity by producing things that look like art but don't involve them—is of course what these routines are about. But such work can have surprisingly violent effects and what is interesting about Home is the way he continues to direct his writing through the present age and its canonical authors, philosophers and artists towards a different kind of future.

Home's is a prose that works against the Eliotic idea of "A people without history/Is not redeemed from time, for history is a pattern/Of timeless moments' (Eliot, "Little Gidding"). In a fascinating essay, Malcolm Bull writes that for Eliot "The equation of ending, apocalypse and fiction is founded on the assumption that 'an end will bestow upon the whole duration and meaning.'" He goes on to assert that, contrary to Eliot, "human time is not made out of chronological time but is, as in Ecclesiastes, 'a time for this and a time for that.' Such times are defined by their purpose rather than their ending." Home is not working to bring about apocalypse. Rather he is the grub-street hack, keeping to the purpose of the time, which is oppositional, disaffected and class conscious. The fertility of Home is that of overworked, pressurised thinking action, a sharp, sweet imagination without a trace of bigotry, intolerance, or exclusivity in its thrust and amplifications.

If Eliotic cultural critics try to keep the republican

imagination restrained within the literary canon, Home denounces the relativists while stating that "saying that all positions are not equal does not necessarily entail a defence of 'canonical literature.'" His novels are more of the same; he plays around, he pranks, takes the piss, using signs that he knows will confuse, upset and outrage anyone with an interest (usually vested) in literature. As he writes in the same essay: "My 'novel' *Slow Death*, and a number of my other 'works', feature 'characters' who adhere to the fashions of the skinhead youth cult... English reviewers often experience difficulty in distinguishing a 'novelist' from the 'fictional' characters that populate his or her books... The notions I utilise—which include 'skinheads', 'pornographic sex', and 'avant-gardism'—should not be viewed as arbitrary but as self-contained signs. Everything done with these signs immediately affects what they are supposed to represent."

The eighteen volume skinhead Bildungsroman written by James Moffatt under the name of Richard Allen and published by the New English Library in the seventies have long been the disreputable bastard father of Home. Clearly, the interest generated by these books for Home works through several of the concerns Home has been investigating and critiquing over the last two decades. The disreputable nature of these pulp trash volumes is clearly attractive to anyone wanting to cause maximum offence to lovers of art writing, those who would assert that they read literature. James Moffatt/Richard Allen is an example of a writer who doesn't write literature. It's against this kind of division that Home is warring. Writing as art, transmitting the eternal, universal load of the author's genius to his/her adoring bourgeois public, is the kind of totalitarian ideology from which Home is dissenting.

The subject matter as well as the style of these books also attracts Home. Violence is a key motif in all the novels, but it isn't just the violence of the soccer hooligan but a violence which extends into the realms of society and sex. Home writes of it as, in an interesting essay "Gender Sexuality and Control: Richard Allen Reconsidered": "... a violence with a dualistic nature. It is simultaneously mechanical and mystical. It is beyond the control of those who vent it, but it is destined to be neutralised by some outside authority, usually the police, at the conclusion of the story... ."

Home is clearly not endorsing the sexism and racism of the tropes in the Moffatt oeuvre, indeed he is explicitly rejecting them, both in the context of essays and his own novels. One way of reading Home's novels is in relation to the Ur-texts of Moffatt. Home is weeding out in his own works those elements of Moffatt which he finds objectionable whilst holding on to and developing those elements which he finds worthy and constructive. So we find him writing that "The heterosexist manner in which Allen depicts adolescent sexuality IS objectionable, but the fact that such sexuality gets depicted at all IS worthy of note." He also argues that because the majority of people reading these novels when they came out were aged between the ages of eleven to sixteen the books' presentation of conflicts with parental authority were of great value. The presentation of deviant values, as a reaction to the failures of do-gooder liberal authority figures such as social workers, teachers and psychiatrists results in a violent, hetrosexualised primitivism and a counter-cultural undercurrent that gives the books their pulse. The reactionary nature of Moffatt's ideological beliefs—his characters are always looking for an authority figure, or some totalitarian tradition to take them in hand—veers very close to being explicitly fascist. These are not the manoeuvrings of some Swiftian satirical imagination: he believed in the stupid stuff. For Home, that "belief" is the enemy. But Moffatt's racy pulp style is undersigned by a detonated, sincere prose and vernacular eloquence. Its fast, energetic readability and the sense of closure attracts Home. They cut against the modern artist's scandalous use of ambiguity and openness which, for Home, are signs of double-think, an inability to communicate, a fetishisation of "difficulty" designed to keep out all but the initiated middle-classes!

What collides in Home's fiction is the brutal efficiency of the pulp prose of Moffatt and the class-conscious sophistication of his own dissenting imagination. The racist, homophobic, sexist, right-wing hierarchical energies of Moffatt are transformed into more socially decent tropes but the style retains its peculiarly angular, knuckly swiftness. Characterisation and the inner life are ejected. Plagiarising Moffatt's books and others, cutting in passages of Schopenhauer, what Home produces is something jumped-up, negligent, seriously funny and funnily serious:

"'You'll never defeat me,' Smith spat. 'You don't even have a theoretical grasp of how to apply the hammer-blow of putsch, let alone the ability to attempt a practical realisation of this deadly tactic. I'm expelling the pair of you from Cockney Nation. And be warned, I'll have you hanged on the day I lead the glorious forces of nationalism to victory. You're just a pair of loonies. Launching an independence movement to liberate Newham is gonna make you a laughing-stock among sincere patriots.' 'Fuck off!' Pat swore as he slammed down his receiver. Brian was exhilarated by this clash of wills. He was rightly proud of the ease with which he'd put down the opposition... .'"

The comedy comes from the brute jamming of the cliched, lefty prose into the mouths of the two speakers. Its deadpan anti-naturalism gives Home the chance to make fun of his character types, but also takes a pot shot at the expectations of the dedicated follower of literature. Every feature of the writing is pulled into the joke, including the imagined reader.

It's clear that this is not writing that simply observes or registers, it demands participation. The usual type of reader exists separately and autonomously in a private space. Reading in that sense is bourgeois, with its structured privacy and individualism. But this writing is dynamic, and demands not a private reader but an audience. In this sense it is erotic writing. And the reader, as pitched in to the drama of the writing, is no longer the middle-class private individual but part of a group. To the decorous, this group might be described unsympathetically as a "mob". Much of the scandal of Home is constructed in the same terms as tabloids writing about groups of strikers.

In *Publishing News*, on 9th April 1999, the story is of 30 printers refusing to print a Home novel, WH Smith and John Menzies refusing to stock it were it to be printed, Scotland Yard's Obscene Publications Squad seizing art work, computer disks and a manuscript and a later story in the same organ of the 7th May explaining that the title would be suppressed from the cover of the book. When finally the book did appear on the Do Not Press imprint, it being too much for the publisher of Home's previous three novels Serpent's Tail, stickers were provided with the title on them which could be stuck on the spine if people wanted. The fact that the supposedly "risk-taking" radical independent publisher Serpent's Tail refused to publish the book is an eloquent example of the commodification of radicalism Home's work confronts.

Home's writing is creating a space to enable understanding and empathy with certain ideas, those concerning the inequalities of the social life as seen from a class perspective, an understanding and empathy usually blocked by the expanding reach of gentility and radical chic. The commodification of dissent, leading to the failure of radicalism to unsettle the dominant discourses, is again and always the issue in the writing. When discussing, for example, talk about a "Scottish literary renaissance" Home astutely points out that even though novelists like Kelman and Welsh would not wish it, in readings of their novels "the notion of the 'street' can be projected into their work and then substituted for the 'peasant' croft as a repository of the 'authentic' and 'earthy wisdom' ... The reductive pastoral discourses remain intact. In style journalism, these reductive literary conventions are often blithely rewritten to fit a hackneyed 'pop' agenda. Instead of being identified with the city, corruption is seen as emanating from those who are fat and old. In this barely revised scheme of things, youth is substituted for the countryside as a repository of 'truth' and 'innocence.'"

Home's novels are attempts to write against this process. They are novels of ideas. As he says somewhere, the process of transformation demands not merely action but also understanding. When he quotes someone saying "Comedy is to slapstick what Literature is to philosophy" he draws the opposite conclusion from that wished for by the writer: slapstick over comedy, and philosophy over literature! In *Whips And Furs: My Life As A Bon Vivant, Gambler*

And Love Rat By Jesus H Christ Edited And Introduced By Stewart Home, he mimics the antics of the James Moffatt of *Satan's Slaves*, working as a photographic negative where the literal meanings are reversed and so gain prophetic infallibility. He's dealing with automatic writing, table tapping, ouija boards, misheard rumours matured into full-blown truth, pub whispers that infiltrated gossip columns then fed back to State Controllers. This is more scandalous than Rushdie's take on Islam; it's a novel where recycled, plagiarised Victorian porn can be substituted for a new take on the life of Jesus. The scandal is about working out just who is been taken for a ride, who is being ridiculed.

The novel is a shock for many reasons, not least because of all the books out on the Attack! Books imprint it is by far the most toned-down and conventionally "literary". Steven Wells, the general editor of Attack! Books, as well as being one of its authors, set up his imprint to challenge the literary establishment from the perspective of left-wing youth. As the star writer for the British music magazine the New Musical Express Wells single-handedly campaigns against racism, sexism, homophobia and other issues, entering into frenzied, hilarious and knock-about debates and rants with the demented glee of a drug-crazed preacher. Paulin's description of Browning's and Hazlitt's prose style could equally describe Wells's: "Nourished in English Dissent, both artists are drawn to an infinitely flexible vernacular expressiveness... They dramatise consciousness in process, and for this they need a syntax and a system of punctuation in which gaps, breaks, shifts, and unexpected changes in vocal texture fluidly embody thinking, feeling, and speaking." Wells's Attack! Books have all exemplified this feature of the English radical dissenting writer, except for Home's book.

Whereas Wells' monumental ranting, beefed-up prose is that of a muscular left-wing Ian Paisley demanding participation, nay communion, from the readership through the fleshy spirit of that language, Home writes in a prose that gains momentum and power from the ideas jammed into unlikely packages and from the jarring contradictions set up between the actual text and the reader's expectations. The excess and the extravagantly lush, roaring prose of Wells burns with all its heart on its rancid sleeve. It's the pugnacious, robust, destructive emotional style of a cranked-up Burke, where eloquence is taken to an insane pitch, abusive, stormy, pregnant with a mass of elements that seem to burst forth into a flux of mental spleen. His writing is, in his own words, like "... James Joyce's *Finnegans Wake* read like Janet and John dumbed down for dyslexics. On Crack." When asked about authenticity, Wells' response was an emphatic, "We're against it."

Home's performance is no less robust and corrosive, but the idiom is yet again of the double-take, the prank, the lie working at the level of an exposure. When, in his mock introduction to the Attack! book, he ventriloquises himself writing as an editor of the text he claims to have discovered on the Internet, which itself purports to be the autobiography of Christ the bluff, double bluff, triple bluff continues to multiply within the idiomatic prose of the mock-scholar. This playing around with a phoney scholarship which he then takes for a walk over the length of the novel, cutting in plagiarised porn, Critical Theory and scathing political comment, generates the book's momentum. It's interesting that the sex, violence and anarcho-sadism of his earlier books are beginning to give way to an emphasis on what he calls "eating, fucking and occultism" and that Home's continuous delight in imposing new rules on himself for each book he writes, deciding on the exact length of paragraphs or chapters he uses for instance, is part of his interest in rhetoric, especially that of extremist political discourse and art as a form of ideology. His interest in occultism stems from his understanding that occultism has been an important part of the dominant Eliotic cultural hegemony. He cites Eliot's use of the occult in his writing of *The Wasteland* to begin an argument in this area.

Home is clear that the remit of mainstream commercial publishers is narrow. It refuses to publish a great deal of material. His deconstruction of various forms of genre writing, particularly youthspolitation, pornography and hard-boiled crime enables him to test out limits. The literary establishment, by which I mean the main publishing houses and the critics who service their output, dismisses Home without really engaging with his inversion of the codes used in real hardcore writing. For instance, in his novel *Slow Death* the man becomes the sex object. As Home himself puts it, "Instead of a woman with curves in all the right places, here's a man with bulges in all the right places."

His latest book, *69 Things To Do With A Dead Princess* finds Home writing for the first time in the first person as a woman. The sex and the occult are all in place, but there's more to do with travel and place names than food here. This psychogeographical treatment seems to have been a particular feature of his last three novels. The essay by Iain Sinclair about Home and his battle with the artist Whiteread in *Lights Out For The Territory* offers some interesting insights into this particular Home routine. Its a book about books, about a fictional non-fiction text called *69 Things To Do With A Dead Princess* by K.L. Callan, about truth and lies and the whole trade. The usual comedy that comes from the immense variety of sex acts in a Home novel is coupled to the immense variety of text acts; page after page of the novel root out, describe, detourne and detonate the intimate ways of readers, writers, publishers and critics.

In it Home can ventriloquise a curiously tender and evocative critical note about eighties novelist Michael Bracewell, which includes the swift, brilliant insight about this bewitching talent: "The eighties ended in economic depression and while Bracewell's early work was marketed as satire, it was ultimately a celebration of middle-class consumerism. Everything had gone wrong and, as St. Rachel documented, it ended in Prozac. Bracewell's flaw was being more intelligent than Cyril Connolly. He knew from the beginning that he was a bad patriot, that the England he lusted after never had and never would exist... " But you also find snide, brief, cutting put-downs of literary star turns such as JG Ballard's *Cocaine Nights*, a novel that "... bristled with middle-brow clichés including an opening sequence that did little more than establish the narrator as a travel writer... No wonder the book had been short-listed for the 1996 Whitbread novel Award."

The sex, the books, the scandal of the dead princess at the heart of the novel's quest (the book of the book is supposed to claim "that Princess Diana's death in Paris was faked and that she's actually been strangled to death Thuggee-style at Balmoral by an unknown assailant") ensures that we are taken on the usual highly idiosyncratic tour of Home's cultural prejudices and comic routines. The experimental ending, where repetition and indexing predominate , bringing a rumour of closure to a novel that ends with "&c. &c. &c." is as good a joke as any Home has yet played. Home knows that his novel has more ideas in it than the so-called "difficult", "serious" "literary" writers whom the cultural establishment lionise.

The genre-bending, the sex and death efficiency of the plot and its prose ensure that once again Home is unsettling preconceived notions of what a novel should be doing. He mouths the words of others in an order that will give them sense. If the truth is unitary—a puritan Protestant conceit perhaps—then its many speakers will all be saying the same thing if they are speaking the truth. To take cognisance of the speaker rather than the thing said is part of the Home joke here. So is the embedded voodoo of a ventriloquist's dummy which is linked in a spooky, tongue-in-cheek hex through the quote from Coleridge at the beginning of the novel : "I regard truth as a divine ventriloquist. I care not from whose mouth the sounds are supposed to proceed, if only the words are audible and intelligible," and the line from a letter from Marx to his daughter Laura dated 11th April 1868, "I am a machine condemned to devour books," to one of the organising themes of the book, which involves truth and access to the truth.

He has somewhere stated that he no longer reads novels for serious stuff, he reads philosophers for that, but here he has written a book which combines a democratic urge to be accessible with an irrepressible appetite for ideas about truth and fiction. It is a novel which lacks the dominant classes' patronising attitude towards working class readers, an attitude which seems to think that the working class is incapable and unwilling to find interest and engagement in anything beyond action. Home's novel is a fierce, violent, unsettling quest for truth. This in itself is a peculiarly old-fashioned quest—so many thinkers have given up epistemology and find quests for "meaning" far more satisfying. His offensiveness is heuristic, well in line with the Lucanian and Machiavellian belief in free speech and turbulent iconoclasm. He's out to provoke a reaction with instincts that are totally opposed to that of the British literary theme park. And of course those who are most aggrieved by this rudeboy are those who would no doubt call the victims of the Peterloo Massacre a yobbish mob and pray for the canonisation of Charles I.

Home's novel *69 Things To Do With A Dead Princess* is published by Rebel Inc. Interestingly, this is a publisher that no longer operates. Home's novels seem to exist in the margins of repression. He manages to play the regicidal wide-boy and just about escapes serious obloquy through obscurity and oblivion. He rides the small-publishing track, working his disputes into a vast and obscure literature that takes shape in the lurid landscape of the cult imagination. His own brief take on his last novel to date has the "body of a dead princess as a metaphor for literature. Works of condensation and displacement. Living out the death of these fantasies in blasted and blistered night, we were consumed by the turning of a page..." Iain Sinclair called Home a serious wind-up merchant. I think "serious" is just about right. He's one of the few novelists writing today seriously trying to reorganise what a novel could and should be doing, knowing with Milton that "fear of change perplexes monarchs" in all spheres of discourse.

THE STRIPPER IN HER NATURAL HABITAT

Jim Ruland

Originally Published: 2001

Magoon knew his relationship with Dawn was over the moment he returned from a bathroom break to his workstation in the data entry department and saw the red light pulsing in his telephone. He stabbed the message button and punched in his password. She wanted him to meet her at Molly's, a decrepit little pub not far from his office. She said it was an emergency.

He navigated the workstation network, sneered at the nosy receptionist, took the elevator to the lobby and made his way across the Tar Pits—his lunch-hour short cut to the pub. His anxiety intensified with each step. Maybe it was the closet paedophile parked on the edge of the gurgling pit, plucking away at a banjo and singing a ditty about a dinosaur with poor bowel control. Perhaps it was the effect the constant revelation of tar had on him, a queasy, nauseous feeling

37

atop his stomach he knew would take several pints of stout to squelch. Or it could have been the pub itself—a place as dark and murky as the prehistoric pit he'd left behind but imagined he could still smell on his clothes, in his hair.

Molly's walls were crowded with old portraits of patrons past. The oily whatness of their easy smiles made him even more anxious. Just last week he had overheard the bartender proclaim that most of the subjects were now dead. The place was packed with shades, ghosts, nevermores.

He heard Dawn's high soft laugh and shuffled toward it. He could almost make her out toward the rear of the pub, and it appeared she had company. A lanky shadow separated from the table where she sat and receded deeper into the pub. Dawn rose to embrace him.

'Sorry I kept you waiting,' he apologized.

'Don't be silly,' she said.

They hugged awkwardly (Magoon was an awkward hugger). She was very tall, taller than he, with a body taut and firm like a trampoline. Her face was framed by thin dark bangs that matched her eyes. Dawn possessed the airy grace of a dancer. She folded herself back into her seat, all fleshy limbs and elastic curves.

Dawn already had a drink. The waiter took Magoon's order and withdrew.

'You look great,' he gushed.

'Thanks.'

'How are things at the club?'

'Great. Really good.' Dawn sipped her beer.

He sensed another dreary afternoon loaded with long silences, pregnant pauses, aborted deferrals to polite conversation. It hadn't always been like this. He could remember when they'd spent hours laughing and drinking together before they went to work. Now their talk subsisted on empty words without passion or purpose, rationed out over the course of the hour. Magoon fished a tattered notebook from his satchel and flipped the pages, finding comfort in the notes he'd scribbled. The light reflecting off the green notepaper gave his face a sickly tint, the face of a drowning man.

The waiter set their drinks before them—Guinness for Magoon, another lager for Dawn—and nearly bumped into her lanky companion as she strode toward the door. He watched her watch him go. He was tall. Broad shouldered. He flashed on the two of them in bed together, the stranger falling on her like a tree. He picked up the glass and slurped at the foam before the stout had properly settled.

'I have something I think we can use,' she announced.

Magoon brightened. Perhaps he'd been wrong about her intentions after all. His pen hovered over the green paper.

'What is it?'

She giggled girlishly. Heads at the bar swivelled in their direction, drawn to the light of her laughter.

'You'll think I'm being a tease.'

'No, I won't,' Magoon insisted. 'Tell me.'

'Okay. One day—Tuesday, before my day shift—I was shaving in the locker room. I swore I would never do that. In front of the girls and everything. I mean, gross! But I did it and Shawna complimented me on my ... you know. There's mirrors everywhere.'

Magoon grunted, draining his glass. He signalled the bartender for another.

'So I complimented Shawna on hers and she told me mine was way better and Selena agreed, which was weird because Shawna and Selena never agree on anything.'

Shawna sported the Betty Page look; Selena had the Gothic-Mistress-Of-The-Dark thing going. Different styles, but the results were eerily the same. Magoon thought they looked like twins, weird sisters.

'Before long.' Dawn continued, 'there were five or six of us standing in front of the mirror, comparing notes. We're going to do hearts for Valentine's Day.'

Magoon tried to visualize the scene, but found his imagination lacking. What did she mean compare? What were the criteria? Coarseness? Triangulation? At last, the waiter returned with replenishments.

Dawn twirled her hair, already bored. 'Anyway, I kind of wanted to talk about something else today.'

Here it comes, he thought, his dread growing. Dawn dipped a lock of hair in his glass and put it in her mouth. Magoon went electric. He lived for these moments, these little one-on-one performances meant for him and him alone.

'I'm going to Paris,' she announced.

'What? Paris? When?'

'My flight leaves Sunday.'

'Is this,' he sputtered, 'something you've always wanted to do?'

'Oh, you have no idea,' Dawn squealed as she brought the glass to her lips. He picked up his drink and sloshed the dark libidinous fluid around the bottom of the glass. She was right. He hadn't a clue.

Her stage name was Dawn, but her real name was Jessica Brandt. They met at the Foxfire Room in North Hollywood, a bar that had teetered on the brink of respectability for so long it had become impervious to bottom feeders like Magoon.

He had been fired from his job as a script developer's assistant earlier that morning and he was getting a jump-start on the celebration. The Foxfire, which opened at six a.m., was the only place he knew would be open. Dawn was the only other customer. He introduced himself and offered to buy her a Bloody Mary, which she rejected three times before she finally relented. He discovered she was a dancer, classically trained. He told her the story of how he got fired for stencilling a handicapped sign in the studio head's parking space, and the story amused her. They spent the day together, lighting up dank rooms all over the Valley. He promised to help her find work. 'I know places,' he told her, neglecting to mention that he was no longer welcome at most of them.

That night, and several double Absolut martinis later, Magoon had her up on stage for amateur night at Hollywood A-Go-Go, a crappy little bikini bar on Cahuenga Boulevard. She stole the show, wowing even the dancers. The top talent, which wasn't saying much, bought her drinks, told her how good she was. Good enough for Hollywood even. She walked out of there with $200, much of it from tips he had persuaded the other girls to give. A stripper was born.

They made love for the first, last and only time in her car that night. Their passion was fuelled by low-grade speed provided by a dancer named Cheri. They got high enough to forget how drunk they were, but their lovemaking was a complete disaster. He could not stay erect. Dawn was helpful at first, eager to please (perhaps too eager, he'd thought) but it was no use. The speed robbed him of his concentration. When they finally gave up, they were sober and hours from sleep. Magoon wanted to go to Mexico, feel the pull of the surf around his ankles while he watched clouds as big as battleships roll in from the sea. Jessica just stared up at the sagging overhead of her decrepit Dodge Dart as if stars only she could see twinkled there. He told her about T.J., Rosarita, Ensenada. It was enough.

Over pancakes at a Burbank diner, they cooked up a plan. She would put her dreams of becoming a dancer, a real dancer, on hold and look for work as a stripper. He would help, he explained, syrup gathering on the tips of his moustache, by documenting

Dawn's experiences in a tell-all Hollywood expose. The book would make them rich and famous, a springboard for bigger things. By their third cup of coffee they were talking movie rights, appearances on Oprah, sipping champagne on a red tile patio overlooking the Aegean.

Her first job was at the bikini bar where it had all started. From there she went on to work at Cheetah's, a topless bar on Hollywood Boulevard. Four months later, she went over to Le Urge, a fully nude gentleman's club on Olympic. With each move she revealed more of her body. It was something he liked to joke about it. 'It's good that we're seeing more of each other,' he told her, but nothing could have been further from the truth.

There was no book. His many failures had taught him to keep his dreams in check and the compromise cost him his ambition. The book was nothing more than a sham, a pathetic ruse. His only desire was to be with Dawn, to never let her out of his sight. Dawn danced. Magoon watched. It was a formula he understood.

Eventually, inevitably, Dawn made herself less and less available to him. She needed sleep, she'd told him, lots of it. The more she worked, the more she slept. Nine, ten hours a day. When she wasn't sleeping, she was with her friends from the club. To fill the days, he reluctantly took a job as a data monkey with one of the trade papers in the Wilshire Corridor. He needed her a great deal more than he knew.

The figure in the portrait hanging above Dawn's head seemed to fix its greasy eyeballs on her. 'You're jealous,' she said.

'No I'm not.'

'You are!'

'When can I see you again?' he asked.

'You can't. I'm picking up extra shifts for the trip. This is it.'

Something came loose inside him. This is what it feels like to go crazy, he thought. 'Just one more time?' he pleaded.

She shook her head. 'I don't know when I'll be back. If I come back...'

'If?' He couldn't believe what she was saying. 'Why Paris? Why now?

Dawn shrugged, lit a cigarette even though there were no smoking signs everywhere. Who could stop her?

'Is it dancing?' he asked.

'Live sex shows,' she said, and there was that infuriating smile again.

The rest of the details came out in a rush. 'I have a friend who did it last year. He said he made a killing.'

'What about the book?

'What book?'

'I'll get an agent. I'll—'

'I've seen your notes. You don't need an agent, you need a therapist.'

Magoon set the mechanical pencil down in the

crease between the two halves of his manuscript. The anger he felt was otherworldly.

'No one goes to Paris in the winter, you stupid whore.'

The bar went quiet. Her eyes flashed and then went dull. For a moment, he imagined he saw what she saw looking down at him from the stage each night. Dawn gathered her things.

'You know what we call you in the locker room?' she asked.

He was pretty sure he didn't want to know.

'We call you The Eunuch,' she laughed. 'Why don't you put that in your book?'

*

Le Urge advertised itself as a European Gentleman's Club, which meant it wasn't run by Armenians like most of the clubs in Hollywood and the Valley. The owners, full-blooded Germans, staffed the place with still more Germans. All the bouncers were big fleshy Teutonic golems with hair the colour of bleached teeth.

At midnight, Magoon got out of his car and crossed the parking lot to the tacky red carpet that led to the club entrance. It was a nice night. A soft breeze made the giant palm that towered over the club waver and sway. A fruit rat scurried along a telephone wire and disappeared in the fronds. The moon was as big as a movie screen.

Dieter and Klaus were working the door. They nodded as he approached. Klaus took his I.D., a card he'd scrutinized a hundred times before, and turned it over in his enormous hands before passing it back to Magoon. Dieter grunted into the telephone headset and let him through.

Inside the club, he skirted the tables around the lip of the stage. The DJ announced a new dancer, Tia Targa, a blonde hardbody from Düsseldorf.

Magoon headed for the curtain that separated the locker room from the club proper. He'd always wondered what it was like on the other side.

He crossed over unseen to the vestibule, the stripper's staging area.

Around the corner he heard voices, a zipper zippering, Dawn's laughter in the upper register.

He held his breath.

He was in.

There was Shawna, Dawn's new best friend, shaving her triangle. Bambi brushed her thick hair. Shayla was bent over her bureau, plugging in the curling iron. Greta stood before a floor-to-ceiling mirror, one of many, adjusting the straps on her bikini, lifting here and pulling there. Vanessa ran a chain through the hoops that pierced her nipples. Janie listened to her Walkman. Selena flipped through a stack of CDs, looking for something new to dance to. And there was Dawn, his beautiful Dawn, sitting at a makeup table just a few feet from where he stood, tapping ashes into an ashtray next to a speckled mirror. On a shelf under the bright bulbs sat a snow globe, and inside the globe, a miniature replica of the Eiffel Tower.

'Dawn,' he stammered, 'don't go.'

He took a cautious step forward into the locker room with the green notebook spread open in his hands. As one, the dancers turned their heads and froze. The hard part is over, he thought. He'd penetrated the inner sanctum, won their attention. Now all he had to do was convince them this wasn't a pervy intrusion, but an expression of his deep and meaningful love.

Dawn picked up the snowglobe and hurled it at him. The globe struck him in the forehead and shattered, releasing its glittery goo. Selena rushed to his side with a small object he thought was a cigarette lighter and let fly with a burst of pepper spray. He went down, rubbing glitter into his eyes, coughing and sputtering, wishing he'd had the foresight to bring flowers.

They formed a circle around him. When the pepper spray cleared, Magoon got the feeling that things were about to go bad in a big way. He tried to stand, and staggered into Janie's half-assed attempt to break a chair over his head. The glancing blow put him down again. He palmed the fragmented tip of the Eiffel Tower and threw it. Then, or so it seemed, a hundred furious women went wild on him, kicking and clawing and pulling his hair. Someone shattered a bottle of Eternity over his head. Another jabbed him with a stiletto heel. They elbowed his nose, kicked him in the teeth, twisted his limbs in impossible geometries. They seared his flesh with the curling iron and ripped the clothing from his body, tearing it to bits. His shoulder popped from its socket. Wobbly stars peppered his vision. Where were those fucking Germans?

In the din he heard Dawn's laugh and he clamped his hands around her neck. He could feel her black heart, that midnight organ, distended and engorged, spasming in her breast. The dancers howled in fury. They pulled him off her and left him writhing on the floor. Then the darkness claimed him—sweet murdered Magoon—and wrapped its foul tentacles around him, dragging him down to a place blacker than tar, sweeter than stout, more beautiful than the shimmering metallic snowflakes that made their way toward him through the fleshy girders of that massive monument to love, settling on his face like a kiss.

ECOSYSTEM DISCOVERED IN SAATCHI'S POCKET

Alistair Gentry

Originally Published: 2002

This work of art (funded by the Arts Council) begins at the end, with a .JPG image of an unknown corpse from the internet.

Their mum was a creative user of the benefits system. The other main thing she always put plenty of work into was refining her smoking technique. Greg and Gary shuffled off to school, there she was at the kitchen table. The palm of one hand glued to her chin, breathing smoke into the sunlight. By the time they came home she might be sitting on the other side of the Formica, but still that bitter smell, still the elbows on the table, still the two fingers pointing like a cocked gun, forty-five degrees towards the ceiling. And smoking.

She was aware of her relationship with her sons, the lack of it, and how she was screwing them up. Couldn't help it. She loitered with the suspicion that she wasn't meant to be a mother before Gary was even born. Eventually mere doubt scabbed into solid conviction. It all ended as badly as everyone expected. When modern houses burn, there's never very much left.

In a flat full of bastardised, mutant dolls and mannequins, Greg wakes up smelling of someone else's anti-perspirant deodorant. His golden fleece reeks of cigarettes. Even from across the room Greg can discern individually the tobacco, the tar, burned paper. When people were allowed to smoke on buses, it used to give his subconscious the terrors. He would have to concentrate just to breathe but he could never get off either, even though he knew he was being stupid.

The window reflects him into one of his own works. A speccy twat with the kind of body most men still have and always will, despite the advertising industry's odes to homoerotic Hellenistic sculpture. Greg isn't effected by advertising. Wearing those pants is a choice, his choice, though Greg doesn't have any arse (sculpted, worked out or otherwise) worth speaking of. Panic attacks him again and his body talks Tourette's, jerking him into closer kinship with the thalidomide dolls he makes. His hands spasm. No musculature worth speaking of allows Greg to wrap arms around himself as his own sobs bounce back to him through the dark.

This month Gary has mostly been annoyed by Met Bar rejects and young black men pretending to talk like Yanks or Yardies. Sometimes they try to do both at the same time. With hilarious results, as they say in the *Radio Times*. People acting hard, putting on personae like they'd slip on once a week shoes. Gary's been to New York a few times, down the estates too, and he's manufactured interest in the tattoos of Russian mafiya-capitalists. Always on quasi-legal business for Rimmington or whoever Rimmington works for. In New York or the sink estates, at a rigged Baltic beauty contest or here, Gary can always spot the real thing. They're the kind of people who can afford to act normal because they really are hard.

The bloke is like a spider, fragile and scuttling hungrily towards Gary on scary thin legs.

'I fink we've met before,' he says, mockney to the max. 'Gary, innit?'

There's a blonde woman too, with the ghost of a black eye. She's almost managed to incorporate the bruise into a makeup job that's simultaneously subtle and theatrical. She's obviously thinking Daryl Hannah in *Blade Runner*, which just shows how deluded people can be. She doesn't speak, doesn't need to because Gary already knows what her voice is like; sheared off and sharpened by expensive education then deliberately worn smooth again by St. Martin's or drama school. She doesn't look the sort to accept a black eye without giving something in return.

'Roke Oh?'

Gary isn't sure what he's being asked. The man is not mistaken, though. They have met before. It's a reminder of his name; Rocco. Gary saw Rocco's critically acclaimed rendition of his own past as a smackhead bisexual, which was also favourably reviewed in the Fringe pages of Time Out. Gary thinks the blonde might be one of the naked, gilded pseudo-lesbians from another play Greg made him go and see. There were two blondes (one real) who stage-punched and pistol whipped each other whilst reciting the names of car manufacturers. Gary supposed Greg's invitation to the play was intended as a type of welcome-to-my-world gesture. Apparently it was OK to look at naked women again because it was post feminist. Gary wouldn't have guessed that what he saw was meant to be post feminist, or post anything else. If he'd known beforehand that it was post-whatever, he probably wouldn't have agreed to go.

Gary remembers finding it impossible to ascertain what they were trying to say, or what it was supposed to all be about, other than just the obvious; middle class drama graduates parading equal measures of nudity and stupidity. To Gary it just looked like a load of people running around the place painted gold, shouting, brandishing cap guns at the audience and generally spazzing about. The contrived gestures of the women, their awkward delivery of found text, and their occasional, partial clothing sometimes placed them vaguely in areas of the erotic with which Gary was familiar. And he had to admit that the gratuitous nudity was an unexpected bonus, though he could have done without all the cocks dangling about.

Rocco and his Goldfinger girlfriend seem desperate to get into the club. Gary doesn't care why, but Rocco keeps dropping Greg's name as if being bought by a Saatchi automatically gives a boy from Braintree coat tails wide enough to accommodate every semi-successful free verse poet and his performance art girlfriend when they fancy carousing with the C list of a Saturday night.

'You see that bitch down there in the stupid coat?' Gary says, indicating the bitch in question, 'She's the one who gets people in. I just chuck them out. It's a he, know what I mean, but don't tell her I told you. So, tell you what, come back when you wanna get bounced and I'll be happy to do the honours.'

The blonde's expression hasn't altered throughout this encounter, which is too realistically staged to be of much interest to her. Rocco's shoulders go, but his head only half turns, as if his torso's got more sense than his mouth.

'Cunt,' it enunciates in profile, then Rocco takes umbrage, blonde and touring accent across the street with him.

Gary knows he shouldn't do what he's about to, but he decides to make an exception for Rocco. It is Saturday night, after all.

'Wait a minute, mate,' he smiles. Rocco trails, too eagerly, back across the street. The woman stands in the opposite gutter with the dog ends and crisp bags, receipts and crushed cans.

Gary's laugh has been infected by his job. His

amusement expresses itself as a rolling bass loop, like a record through a wall. Rocco seems almost hypnotised by Gary's laughter, staring up at him, Mediterranean lips slightly parted— until the crack of nasal cartilage. For Gary it's one of the most enjoyable aspects of working in the security industry. You get so many opportunities to express to people, immediately and unequivocally, exactly how you feel. Call it alerting them to their position in the pecking order. Or call it nutting them hard in the face.

Cal is scampering around Greg's flat, still pretending that he's got no arms. Greg feels hungover, though he wasn't drunk last night. Nauseous, fragile and tension headache. He's not sure whether it's from squinting through the viewfinder for the hours it took to get what he wanted, or just Cal's draining presence. Cal is trying to put his T-shirt back on without using his hands. Greg plans to render him in fibreglass as a skinny, hyperactive boy with big pores, aggressive eyebrows, white Y-fronts and no arms.

'Can I have one of these?'

Cal's holding a spool of red peel-off labels with HELLO MY NAME IS printed on them, the product of an idle morning spent wandering around Staples. Greg nods, anything for a quiet life, take as many as you like. Cal finds a black marker that almost works. In the space underneath HELLO MY NAME IS Cal writes DEATH, then sticks it over his heart.

'Been up to see Rocco's show yet?' Greg asks, more for something to say than out of any interest. Cal shrugs in what he thinks is the style of an amputee.

'I've decided I'm not going to associate with any-one whose childhood predates Space Invaders,' Cal answers, no answer at all.

'Oh, right. And what are you going to be if you grow up?'

Cal frowns, grins, frowns again. Greg's face isn't giving him any clues.

Courtney arrives and Cal buzzes her up without asking Greg's leave. Courtney is a clone of Cal's last girlfriend, as she was of the one who preceded her. Dyed hair, cropped, given to erring on the streets of the city and blaming it on postgraduate study. Her el-bows are conspicuously marked up with carpet burns. She's been making arty farty sex films with Rocco for about a year. Greg isn't sure whether this constitutes a steady relationship or not. Sometimes Courtney fucks Cal in the films, but the fact that she also fucks him off camera still seems strangely akin to adultery. If anybody felt sorry for Rocco, they might drop a hint or two. The trouble is, Rocco devotes awesome energy to courting misfortune and woe. Virtually everything in his life is done with the intention of it being a bad experience he can turn into material. So nobody tells Rocco. They just don't want to give him the satisfaction.

Courtney demands attention as well, photographic and otherwise. She seems to imagine that without it she would evaporate into anonymity, that eventually her image might degrade into invisibility. That's why she photographs herself, supple and naked, on the Underground. As if she is in a short story, as if to illustrate characterisation, when Courtney catches Greg's eye momentarily he finds that he is smiling feebly like he's done something he shouldn't have. Courtney hardly smiles back, but then she hardly smiles ever.

Courtney and Cal go at each other with a no-tomorrow zeal that makes even Greg cringe. From behind Cal's ear, Courtney catches Greg's eye again.

'I know what you're thinking,' she says, disengaging her lips from Cal's. 'Everyone knows that Rocco's a shifty, manipulative, dirty old pervert. Total fucking perv turned up to eleven. I mean, I don't have a problem with that, but he doesn't own me or anything.'

'Yeah,' agrees Cal, 'Any fucker that chides us for having feelings can suck our cocks.'

Greg concedes to himself that— for what it's worth— Courtney and Cal are probably in love.

Rocco has an Elastoplast across the bridge of his broken nose. He forgot to take it off before he went on. Somehow the innocent little plaster undermines that night's performance of *I'm an Anagram of Everything*. A small audience observes with metropolitan apathy, even when Rocco invites them to feel his pain by recreating the addiction and self-abuse of his formative years using multiple syringes and a straight razor. Rocco gets through plasters like nobody's business. He buys them from the Cash and Carry.

To be fair, Rocco's verse crackles along with the

kinesis of machine gun fire. To be honest, his poems about power, greed and sex shops are an embarrassment. When he sees Courtney, Cal and Greg in the auditorium, Rocco waves, mid sentence. This is unprofessional and not very cool.

Afterwards Greg tells Rocco that he loved the show, &c. Inadvertently he apologises for the destructive capabilities of his brother's forehead. It just slips out, violating no-charity-for-Rocco protocols.

'S'OK,' Rocco shrugs, 'If I'd met meself last Saturday I wouldn't have been very impressed either. Actually I'd probably have 'eadbutted meself.'

'Why'd you act like such a cunt, then?' This is a very poor attempt at disguised hostility from Cal.

'I'm not in control of what I do,' Rocco says with an audible shrug. Cal sneers.

'Oh, how silly of me—'

Rocco lights a cigarette and then asks,

'Mind if I smoke?'

'Care if I die?'

Greg's thought of this beforehand, and he thinks he probably stole it from somewhere, but it's a great goal nonetheless. Rocco looks almost shocked.

'Alright, chill out.'

Rocco takes three huge drags on the ciggie, smoking it in about five seconds, then stubs it out under the rim of the table. Greg brushes stray ash from his trousers.

'Why do you think Marlboro County's always empty in those adverts?'

He shoots, he scores. It's a rewarding job, helping Rocco to keep his ego reasonably restrained. Cal obviously wants to clap with joy like a groovy Christian, but for once he manages to control his retarded urges. As usual Courtney just sits there holding a beer bottle at arm's length like it's going to explode, not doing anything to get the conversation back on its rails.

Greg recognises a face on the other side of the bar, a journalist from *The Guardian* against whom Greg's got an ongoing grudge. Greg made the mistake of informing Cambridge Boy that his influences were "Special Brew and the studied unreality of Soho and Brighton". The article had set this gem as a pull quote next to a picture of Greg looking New Brit Artish and rather munting. When Greg saw it he vowed to shit down the guy's neck without even tearing his head off first.

'Yeah, I'm still doing drugs,' drones the hack to everyone within earshot, 'But I've decided to do them ironically.'

Can Greg keep it dignified, gentlemanly, out of the tabloids? Find out next week.

Everyone's shoved up against a wall watching Rocco taping Cal pumping Courtney. Greg doesn't pay much attention to the enthusiastic method-foreplay, or to Rocco's directions. What Greg is fascinated by are the scrapes on Courtney's elbows and the bruises on her hips. She looks like she's fallen off a skateboard or something. Though she's knocking thirty it's not inconceivable. There's a woman called Kate next to him. She's from Courtney's theatre company. Apparently she's something to do with devising the film. The working title is *Blood Bath*. Kate has just realised that the whole thing's more porny and less theatrical than she anticipated. By way of indicating her dismay, she turns to Greg and whispers,

'It kind of smells in here.'

She's right. Greg doesn't tell her that the stench is from some dead seagulls. Rocco went through a phase of painting them until he got bored and left the birds to rot in his spare room. Typically, his neighbours were more distressed than Rocco was. When they complained he just threw the rancid bird carcasses into the street.

Some funding is allegedly imminent. Rocco submitted sheaves of documentation explaining in a hundred different ways that it wasn't going to be essentially a Playboy Channel thing like the last one. Cal starts whining about wanting to go. He's hungover from AM drinking. Courtney wanders off into the kitchen while Rocco is distracted.

'*Star Trek* is on in a minute,' Cal says, 'And I'm sorry, but it's one of those events I have no power to control. I have to watch it for research purposes.'

Rocco angrily shoves the camera into Cal's face. Cal isn't sure whether this is still art.

'Just once I'd like to hear something other than a complaint come out of your mouth,' says Rocco.

Cal is profusely sick over Rocco's feet.

'Get out!' Rocco screams. The room is far too small

for Kate and Greg to escape.

'Wait...' Cal mutters. 'One other thing—'

Cal vomits again. Rocco launches heavy-duty invective, some of it in whatever his mother's language is. When he's run out of abuse he looks as if he's going to hurl the (rented) camera as well until Kate prises it out of his grip and backs away as if she's under heavy shelling. Rocco hardly seems to notice. Cal says he's a trained actor and if he wanted to take this kind of shit he would have joined Equity so at least he'd get the union minimum and subsistence.

'Fuck you,' shouts Cal's retreating back. 'Fuck you and your art. And your girlfriend.'

Exeunt Cal, Courtney and Kate. Rocco slides his back down the wall until he's in a crouch.

'By projecting your anger,' he proclaims to the recently slammed door, 'You will never examine your life.'

It's hard to believe, but this statement is even less profound than it seems. Greg knows it is just the title from one of Rocco's performance pieces, and Rocco didn't even think of it himself. He just read it on the wall of the gents' lav at the ICA.

'Go go go!' Rocco shouts, wriggling like an impatient child, sloshing water everywhere. 'This is it!'

Courtney is behind the camera this time.

'Can we hurry this up?' she says, 'This is my *Buffy* tape, it's a really good tape I'm taping over, so can we get a move on?'

Rocco stares the lens down, one hand absently trying to tug some life into his dick so it doesn't look so small under the water.

'The silence begins to get to you,' he says. 'It whispers in your ear, lets you in on a secret. Tells you this isn't a real game. They ran away to play a different game. The game they all really wanted to play. Without you.'

Greg, Courtney, Kate and Cal watch Rocco maul, punch, scratch and cut himself in meaningless fury. Sometimes he emits incoherent strings of almost-words, the sounds a brain makes as it comes unglued. Blood pours down Rocco's back, trickles from his neck and mats the hair of his chest, runs into his eyes from his cut forehead. He starts to twist and thrash from side to side like a fish drowning in air. Airborne splashes Pollocking the tiles. Courtney doesn't want to get dripped on, she backs into the toilet and sits down hard on the seat. Rocco tries to stand, his hands seek her, slips off balance, legs in the air, his face goes under the red red water.

There is another ellipsis in the narrative.

The picture of Doorman Gary: grown up with the five o' clock shadow to prove it, but still the real big brother, driving silently to the place he knows, the place someone he knows who works for Mr Rimmington knows, the place where they can get rid of Rocco. For a few days Greg couldn't stop crying. Now he thinks he's just about managed to disconnect from the whole thing. It happened with an almost audible click while he was momentarily distracted by a new Levi's advert. Courtney and Kate took turns at sitting in shocked, useless silence round each other's flats. Nobody even asked where Cal disappeared to. Yesterday he rematerialised and said he wanted to help Gary and Greg.

Even though Greg knows what is inside the black plastic and elephant tape, he feels like he could or should hold it. It's a dead body, Rocco's thoroughly kosher corpse, but Greg has an irrational urge to give the parcel a hug because it looks so sad. Greg knows he doesn't really want to touch the thing, he just feels lost and he needs to hold somebody. It's meant to be romantic, fucking yourself up. It isn't romantic at all.

The four of them— Greg, Courtney, Cal and Kate— decided they weren't going to the police. Courtney's camerawork is so shit that the tape doesn't really show anything until after Rocco is dead. Ever tried explaining art to a copper? So they thought it would be easier for everyone and save on repercussions and gaps in their CVs if they just buried Rocco somewhere. The rest of them assume that Greg will be able to sort it. After all, he is the only one of them who used to be working class.

Gary sits half out of the car, idly rubbing out bootprints in the mud with his toes. The cigarette making rapid circuits to and from Gary's scar of a mouth is the only sign of nerves needing to calmed. Cal is listening to his Walkman, not happy or flippant but making urgent little bobs of his head, as if breakbeats can dislodge what he's done. Greg hears the first diffident bird of morning and wonders what the ratio is of bodies buried to bodies found.

Photographs are meant to provide proof of identity, to capture some version of the reality of things, but Greg never recognises himself in them. That's why the picture in *The Guardian* was disappointing. Not because of that stupid caption, or turning the page to see the usual fashion spread of dead-eyed 12 year old anorexics in strappy dresses and makeup by Stevie Wonder. It was because the picture of Greg didn't bear any resemblance to him at all. He always feels let down by photos of himself.

The image in the browser doesn't look like Rocco either, doesn't look like anyone. A screen grab. Legs splayed with the studied carelessness of habitual nudes. Armpit submersed. The arm almost looks detached because of the way it's flung up and out. New cuts across old ones on the hairy belly and chest, scratching out the final draft of an illegible suicide note. Face out of frame. Greg knows who it is. The body doesn't need a head.

Click. He disconnects. With an audible click.

MARYLAND

Steve Aylett

Originally Published: 2002

'Never thought I'd find a skeleton like this in my beef.'

'Damnedest thing.'

'Well, here's Henry at last.'

A cage car careened through the scene tape and slewed up. Chief Henry Blince thrust open the door, a chairleg cigar in the middle of his puffy face, and lurched out, breathing the night air. 'I can taste this arrest already. Shot in the pump?' He frowned at the firework flashes of a press gaggle.

'Henry,' said the Mayor cheerfully, 'you know Jack.'

'Bang on the border, looky here—the Mayor, Harpoon Specter and the Chief o' Terminal in a dustcoat!'

'Oh, I don't think Mr Coma claims any jurisdiction,' said the Mayor with a nervous smile.

'You bet your sweet life he won't.' Blince lumbered past the three men and regarded the body, its third eye as open as a gas-blown manhole. 'It's a keeper. Got any leads?'

'Waiting for you, Henry. Even Jack here.'

'Coroner'll wanna know.' Blince gestured at the press. 'Get the rag-and-boners outta here and secure the scene. Didn't they teach you that in cop college, Jack? Got a downer on this guy?'

'I don't need downers, Henry.' Coma struck a match and lit a shock absorber. 'I'm low on life.'

Harpoon Specter was squinting at Blince, amused. 'You don't get it, do you Henry?'

Blince removed the cigar from his face like a fork from a hog. 'Eh? Why the big deal? You made any money?'

'Only thing I've made is up my mind who to represent.'

'Here's Rex Camp and the Doc. Real mare's nest o' activity. Hey, Mangrove—calamari earrings?'

But no sooner had the Coroner and Doctor Mangrove reached the body than a white truck roared up and began unloading. A guy in a robe hovered out of the smoke. 'You are forbidden to touch the body.'

The Mayor began wringing his hands. 'Henry, this is Mr Wingmaker, head penguin of the church cartel.'

'Well I'm sorry you feel that way, padre.'

'That's not the point.' Wingmaker looked at the body, wide-eyed.

'Order your examiners away from there.'

'On whose authority?'

'I have a cartel gag disguised as a court order.'

'So you went to the perjury room. Like some kid cryin' to teacher.'

'It's true,' muttered Wingmaker, then pushed the medics aside.

'Take a look, Mr Blince. This could be the biggest religious event since Saint McCain.'

Blince looked from Harpoon Specter's smile to the body. The blood pool around the victim's head had formed the classic shape of the Blessed Virgin in prayer. Wingmaker's men were already erecting a prefab chapel around the body.

'Oh, well ain't that dandy,' growled Blince. 'I realise, padre, you don't know one end of an identity parade from another. But John Doe here has a punishin' schedule o' decay to keep irrespective o' your goddamn celestial blockade. Now that's a hell of a blowfly opportunity.'

Doctor Mangrove walked past with her toolbox. 'Order checks out, Chief. Got nothing but the obvious.' Rex Camp followed her, morose.

'Same order against our examiners, Blince,' said Jack Coma. 'We'll subpoena the rags for them press photos.'

'Well, you're thinkin' like a cop at last.'

'Position of the body, this apparition came from our side of the border.'

'Body did.'

Coma turned away. 'Apparition.'

Blince and Harpoon Specter were walking back to the cars. 'What's your angle, Harpo. You gettin' pious on us?'

'When it pays.'

'When's that.'

'With this blood here I think we got a bona fide miracle on our hands.'

'Ain't on mine.'

'Remember years back them elephants in India drinkin' milk?'

'So what? I can drink milk to beat the band. That a miracle?'

'Them animals were made of stone. Stone, Henry, you hear what I'm sayin'?'

'Aw, hell, it's all in the mind.'

'Well, thank god,' chuckled Specter, 'an unimportant organ.'

Blince reached the cop car and re-lit his cigar. A trooper waited at the wheel. 'Well, I'm goin' for a bagel and a vat o' the heart o' darkness. Wingmaker was generous enough to gimme access to one fact, bless him. See the hoofprints around the hearse ballast?' He ducked into the car. 'Blank as a model.'

'Perp works the kinda place they don't allow tread on your shoes. Harder to run.'

Blince slammed the door and the car growled away.

'Office,' muttered Specter.

It was in fact a year since Johnny Failsafe had put a seashell to his ear and heard mocking laughter.

He'd become his own boss by a florid and circuitous route. Somewhere along the line he'd got it into his head that he was more than a pewter figurine in a pewter cubicle. He'd read about poor folk in the old days who'd get a little support by losing their ID and staggering near the German border to pretend they'd defected. And he was fascinated. It seemed everything could change at a border. At the Mexican one, Americans changed into Nazis. So he quit the office and started walking out of Beerlight and across Our Fair State, kicking up dust till he reached the Terminal border. This was a little before the break-up of states and there were no emplacements—just Johnny Failsafe stepping back and forth across the line, trying to detect the subtle sensation of the laws changing around his body. He thought he perceived the smallest shift in the pressures upon him, but so what? He was still being worked on. He knew that once upon a time Leon Wardial had hacked statute and added laws—incrementally at first, and then in an exponential swelling which had obliterated the last vestiges of human activity. Weeding the authorised admonitions from the random additions was a mind-bending, year-long task.

One spokesman appeared before the press laughing and hitting himself in the face with a thundery sheet of aluminium. Nowadays authorised statute saturation made the Trojan Law prank redundant. But Failsafe became obsessed with that transition point at the border, where one barrage of restrictions gave way to another. Was there a point between the two—however minute—where neither were present? He knelt at the state line squinting into a microscopic earth seam filled with animated freedom. A sample retrieved in a core tube showed a swarming heaven under magnification and Failsafe took to sinking two perspex sheets to extract a thin borderline sandwich. An everyday torch could project the lawless activity onto a wall and Failsafe biffed over to Don Toto at the Delayed Reaction on Valentine.

'Ever seen a tornado, Toto? Incinerator, my abrupt friend. Light shows nuthin'. I think you're ready for the bright stuff. The salient stuff.'

'Saline? Sounds good.'

Failsafe put a sheet in front of a stage light and the wall went all to sherbet, roiling like the face of Jupiter.

'It's boisterous, Johnny.'

'It's automatic, what it is. And for but a few clams will take the edge off this ominous shit you seem to love so much.'

'It is ever-changing.'

'It'll give the clientele a hint of higher matters, Toto.'

'Nevertheless, I'll take it. Name your price, you sick mother.'

Failsafe began a roaring trade in border samples, which formed light shows in clubs from Greada's to the Creosote Palace. He started shipping to clubs coast to coast, including MK-Ultra, a Monarch-themed dive in Pittsburgh where the clientele attended as two or more different people and paid accordingly at the door. The owner Ned Wretched saw how ELF battled off the visuals to create a unique feel. It wasn't like the old police-and-thieves, where the only muddy hint of colour was squeezed from the narrow act of interpretation. Fizz geeks flooded in, and Ned decided to steal Failsafe's manufacturing secrets and make a bundle. He was surprised when, under cover of darkness, Failsafe drove out to the border in an armoured dune buggy and knelt on the pumice ground, slotting a cross-section panel into the earth like an exposure plate. Startled banter and a struggle between the two entrepreneurs ended with Ned Wretched dead of his own gun and Failsafe all festooned with dread. He glanced out his window on Salad Street and saw the dreaming spires of damnation. His prints were on the gun. The gun was under the body. And on TV a tale unfurled of a mystical image blossomed out of Wretched's head. The crime scene was a mecca for gawpers and a penguin offered saintly protection and media cache to the killer.

Weird twilight and Failsafe visited a friend on pale Saints Street.

'Way to screw up, Johnny,' said Atom as Failsafe entered his office. He lit a shock absorber. 'Jeans and a tie? Look like a gypsy at a funeral.'

'Anyway you owe me, Atom.'

'The bigger bones float. Siddown, Johnny. I assume that gun was coin-operated—real economical.'

'There was a struggle, the gun went off.'

'That'll happen. Know the rarest and cheapest thing in the world? A gun that ain't been fired. Smoke?'

A pair of chunky glasses lay on the desk, trailing wires.

'That some kinda Walkman?'

'It's a Vollmann. Put it on, close your eyes and you think you're changing the world. You gun hunting? You know better than to come to me.'

'I know better than to get you on the case too, Atom. Need to borrow a cloaking system.'

'What's the venue, the demographics.'

'Law, church cartel, press. Guess it's a headcharge.'

'No, from a certain angle you'd see they're all faced the same way. Take a look at this.'

Atom activated a wall panel and retrieved a weird piece of kit. It looked like the black cobra headdress of an Egyptian prince.

'What is it?'

'Diamondback. It's a classic denial-allow hood—broad-spectrum bigot challenge with a billion-image chip library. Old and clunky but it's all I've got to hand. You'll have to keep it simple.'

'So it projects whatever the onlooker can't afford to acknowledge?'

'Sure. Quiet-life technology's come a long way since the old log cabin, my friend. Good luck.'

Private cloaking systems had kicked off when an inventor found he could go anywhere and be ignored so long as he carried a charity can. Now Failsafe walked invisibly out of the night and through the crowds at the crime scene. It was a media event, all harsh arc lights and generalisation. He followed unseen behind Chief Blince and a trooper as they approached the chapel.

'They servin' a catered lunch at this murder, Benny? Eh? Too bad. I could do with a couple hotdogs.'

'Got any leads, Chief?'

'That bad, eh? Guess we better concentrate on the case, trooper boy. Single Shot to the Head Syndrome. No gun on the scene. All we really know by the stellate tearin' round the blowhole is it was some kinda fancy I.D. grip etheric.'

'Coffee table gun.'

'Yeah. This was nuthin' to do with money, theft or clubland, that's for sure.'

'You reckon the killer's the guy's wife?'

'Far as I'm concerned it's a given.'

'A gibbon? Why would anyone marry a gibbon?'

'A given, Benny, I mean it's obvious.'

'Not to me, Chief.'

'And meanwhile Wingmaker's little amnesty's attractin' a whole lotta wannabes.'

'Ain't wallabies jumpy animals?'

'You said it. And they ain't foolin' me.' They entered the chapel to find a rogue's gallery crowding the corpse. A massive electric fan battled with the bluebottles. 'Well, a real tea party. Anyone else comin' round to laugh it up?'

'Blince,' nodded Jack Coma, his face expressionless.

'See what I mean, Benny? Amateur hour.'

'Too many cooks for yuh Henry?' Specter smirked. 'Somehow it don't seem possible.'

'Who's your client.'

'Fish in a barrel, Henry. Very least I could trace a family for the pulse loser, get a fractal compy.'

'Sure, the poor lamb. Blood o' the innocent—Brady material. And with Wingmaker here not allowin' removal, a lotta scope for distress and the like, yuh goddamn shyster.' Blince chuckled, lighting a cigar.

'Mister Blince,' Wingmaker protested, 'this is a blessed site.'

Blince grunted. 'This is a blessed mockery, padre. I seen a million spills—they all look like somethin'. I remember after the NLP riots, I saw a puddle looked just like Benny here, sat on some kinda dinosaur. I didn't see any goddamn media frenzy that night. So quit stuffin' words o' love in my ears.'

'This here body's slung right along the state line, Mister Blince,' stated Coma. 'I'm claiming equal jurisdiction.'

'Well, Sherlock.' Blince considered his cigar, frowning. 'Just how much trouble are you used to?'

Failsafe approached the body. As he moved in the crossgrains of the law, he was seen as a defiance so massive it could not be acknowledged. An alien, a yeti, an invisible man—it couldn't be here and it wasn't. Chuffed, Specter dumped his briefcase on the prefab altar and flipped the catch. 'God, I love this. Chessboard's all pawns, Henry. Stir in your black budget taxes and the board gets grey. I'm even inclined to represent the old girl herself here. Wouldn't that be something?'

'Somethin',' Blince muttered. He was frowning at the air in front of him. 'Somethin' strange.'

Failsafe stepped onto the state line, that slim territory free of external manipulation. As he straddled the body, he was a figure of phosphene flux, lightning in a bottle—for a brief moment the hat polarised and everyone saw what they wanted to see. Attention poured into him. Wingmaker saw the Lord himself bestow a benediction on the corpse. Coma saw a con from his jurisdiction confessing all and more. Specter saw a photogenic psychopath screwing the corpse and saying society made him do it and he wanted legal assistance. Henry Blince saw a combination of all three combined with his mother. 'Ma,' he said, lurching forward and stopping, fish-eyed. 'You brought pancakes?'

'Don't answer that,' snapped Specter.

'The Lord has no use for pancakes, heretic!' screamed Wingmaker.

'They're stolen,' stated Coma.

'And why not,' said Benny, seeing someone refreshingly justified and innocent.

The headset fell from Failsafe's head as he retrieved the Colt Double Edge and he stood straight into visibility.

'Well don't that take the cherry,' muttered Blince, slack-faced, then he grinned. 'It's the perp, with an old-fashioned Zeus cap. Welcome to the party, boy.' He drew an AMT Automag. 'Now step away from the miracle and drop the flaw.'

Failsafe dropped the Colt and jittered forward a little, hands raised.

'Stop where you are, boy,' Coma shouted, pointing a 41-clip Giuliani.

'He's mine, Coma—couple millimetres over the line.'

'You're meddling with knowledge as ancient as a carp, Mr Blince,' shouted Wingmaker. 'This man is under the church's protection—take your finely-crafted differences outside.'

'I'd be failing in my public duty if I didn't punch your eye right now, padre.'

'It was an accident,' pleaded Failsafe.

'Real poetic,' Blince chuckled. 'Look close you'll see little parachutes on my tears. You're the only candidate's rolled up in secret, mister. That gives you the guilt.'

'No reasoning with nature's balloon there,' smiled Specter, approaching Failsafe. 'You're an innocent man and you need a friend.' Failsafe reached reflexively to his head—was he still wearing the headgear? Coma grabbed him suddenly from behind, dragging him back across the line. Then they were all upon him, jerking him this way and that like a sap.

'Allow me to introduce myself!' Specter was yelling as he pushed his card at Failsafe's face like a communal wafer.

'Couldn't take no for an answer could yuh?' bellowed Blince.

'Mercy seat's waitin', boy!'

'When he dies I want the mineral rights!'

'You've a right to be angry, lad!'

'Tough but fair!'

'Unauthorised murder, bless him!'

'Life and change!'

'My client is enigmatically innocent!'

'His pants are expensive!'

'I got the same number o' legs—think there's a connection?'

And under their scuffing feet the brown Madonna was knocked and tilted—glancing down they saw the phasing shapes of a monster truck, a flightbag, pond dice, inflatable hammers, a pig in a tyre-swing, an inarticulate outcast, a wily sheriff containing the answers, a map of Denmark, a camel, a weasel, a whale. Bursting in, the press did the rest.

Failsafe improvised an alibi with such breathtaking verisimilitude that the cops asked him aghast if it really was a mere product of his fancy. The press called him The Bullshit Killer. A befuddled Wingmaker spoke of Failsafe as 'our own little ray of sunshine'. Blince gave a statement that 'This is a good world—I joined the force to make a difference. Anyhoo, I want him in lavender.' Out of respect to the deceased, Specter proposed ten years' silence on the truth of the matter. The President gave a speech recommended for ages 2 to 6. Bewildered into madness by these proceedings,

Failsafe was sat among other blanks on floor-bolted chairs, lip-reading cartoons with the sound down. The lines blurred. By the time all the attention had moved on, even he'd forgotten who he was, and the bars of his window had merged with the shifting shapes in the sky.

HALLUCINATION = CELL

Kenji Siratori

Originally Published: 2002

to the fingertip of the marionette=brain cell of the embryo that accumulates the happiness type of the past of an artificial paradise on the gimmick of the drug mechanism of the angel that my soul begins to split on the brain of the murder of an ant the cell wolf toys with the cyber=aerofoil of the clone catastrophic internal organ of the blue sky quark the transmission line of the cadaver city plays to the mode of life clonic passion of birds discloses the DIGITAL_generative organ to the vocal cord with the bio=less_air of an embryo sun that the stratosphere of the happiness of a chromosome consciousness of the micro murder that was done the drug*reproduction gland of the blue sky my gimmick that cracks to the accomplice of the velocity of light=inheritance of death god who DNA is diverging like the guerrilla of the cell of the ant interference to the map on the other side of the sun desire and was made the eradication of the hell of the cell the honeycomb of TOKAGE BABEL visual hallucination send back out the fission disease of the sun to DIGITAL to the cell other selfs that dance earth outside circle=of where my brain basement of the embryo in the annihilation just before LOAD=to the splendid suspension of the baby-universe that ill-treats the hope of the ants of the future tense to the chromosome and interchange the word of the fatalities to the rhinoceros bar crime net of ADAM the brain of a dog the infinite embryo of the graviton the sun that the emotional particle that idles was crossed—to magnetaito of f/0 of the cadaver that inherited the synapse of etc of the god straightfowardly desire! the end of the cell the DIGITAL_aerofoil of the brain of the madman to the eye of the synapsetic rhinoceros of the embryo that creates the intention of the rhinoceros bar murder of the cloud to my velocity of light=storage of the immortality that flutters to the murder medium of the lightning speed of anti-faust and recover the hell of the micro=larva guerrilla is my soul done to the chaosmic=cyber of BABEL infinite divergence and the cell war of the hell of the sun in the outer space of the brain of an embryo gimmick bisexually?? to my inorganic substance=caress that does not know you who the word bursts to the crisis of 1 micron of a vital body and fly! the respiratory organs of the childish apocalypse are jointed to the pupil of the DIGITAL_girl!

THREE POEMS

Billy Childish

Originally Published: 2002

the strangest thing

today dolli isn't hard and arrogant
she isn't puffed up and bitter
i can hear tiredness and a tremour
in her voice

she wants to know
if she can
come and visit me
things aren't working out between her and her
new boyfriend

-ive been in margate
visiting my mum
it reminds me of when we were together

you were the first great love
of my life
now theres M
youre the same in lots of ways
hes fucking these stupid little art sluts
theyre fucking nobodys!
i tell him
theyre fucking
nothing compared to me!
but he still does it
i need to talk to you
if it tell my friends in
london
that I want to kill myself
theyre not interested
they don't want to know about that part of me
its really doing my fucking head in!
you know
my mum said the strangest thing to me last night
she said that it doesn't matter if things don't work
    out
between me and M
because you can get back together again with billy
i said -
but mum what about kyra? He's still with kyra
    mum
and she said that that dint matter
we arrange a time to meet and I replace the re-
    ceiver

no
this girl isn't hard and arrogant
she is lost and alone
and somehow
i wish I could have been kinder to her

a terrible thing

when keerah was 22
she found that she was 12 weeks pregnant
she looked at me with fear in her eyes
- what shall I do?
- She asked me
- its up to you I said
- ile support you in whatever dessision you make

I looked out of the garden window
i thought I was being so holy
so decent
so understanding
but I didn't stop to look inside
and to treat her with enough respect
to make the demands of what I wanted

i was to bissy being (understanding?)
in truth I was too young
too drunk
and too tied into my own dream
of hell
to know my own heart

i failed myself
i failed keerah
and I faild our unborn child
who I kiss now
with this poem

i am the strange hero of hunger

my girlfriend lives
on the other side of the world
and
has
started
reading
crime and punishment
by fydor dostoyevski

do you recognise the main characicter?
i ask her excitedly
- doesn't he remind you of me?

-ive only just begun
she answers
whats his name?

-rodya
but all the characters
have about 3 different names
i always get confused
and
cant tell who is who
because im dislexic and don't make sounds for the
    names
but rodya is for short
and
his sister is called dunya

isn't dunya a butiful name?
if little huddie had been born a girl
we would of named her
Dunya
when I talk of the buti
of girls names
or the strange bravery
of artists
or see
the lite change
over sea
and sky
every second impossible showers of
gold
turning to terrible hues of purple
and
black
and
my
hart rate quickens
because
i am amongst
my
own
people

i am
the hero of all my favourite novels
i live in them
and they

live in me
i am Arturo bandini
on angels flight
swearing at a butiful dark haired girl
in tattered shoes
i am rodya
guilty of a terrible and senceless murder
on the streets of st peterersburg
i am the strange hero of hunger
starving to spite myself in christiana
i am johan nagel
tormentor of the midget
and suiside
i am ishmail
knocker off of tall hats
i am every novelist
and
every character ever dreamed
i am everyone of my favorite artists
and
i feel myself not one jot less
but equell to all of them
Turner
Munch
Holbine
and
Hokusi

naturally I have no heros
i am my heros

i am my brothers
and sisters
i feel myself joined by the soul
with all buti
my hart sings with every brave endevor
with the strange wings of impossible butterflys
with every rock that breaths life into the world

i stand shoulder to shoulder with
all denouncers of meaness
i honour spirit and faith
and I uphold the glorious amiture
i am in love with desperate men
with desperate hands
walking in 2nd hand shoes
serching for god
and
hearing god
and hating god
i am a desperate man buckled with fear
i am a desperate man who demands to be listend
   to
who demands to connect
i am a desperate man who denounces the dullness
   of
money
and status
i am a desperate man will not bow down to acolayed
   or

success
i am a desperate man who loves the simplicity of
    painting
and hates gallarys and white walls and the dealers
    in art
who loves unreasonableness
and hot headedness
who loves contradiction
hates publishing houses
and
also I am Vincent van gogh
hiroshige
and every living breathing artist
who dares to draw god
on this planet

THREE POEMS

Mike Watt

Originally Published: 2002

the swelter I felt there

I
labored
over and debated
voicing
every
yearning and
outburst in my daily chimping,
urging my most
econo
language
instead of the
zeal
angled spiel
but then thought, "fuck it"

eventually evolving
to
hear it
shoveled into a coal train's load
of dream fuel
brain spooled
so tight
it sprung—ho!
...popped!
w/the thought
hmm...
such a very serious look:
your eyes narrowed
brows furrowed
hands gestured
as to measure
significance
and accent
just what
is to be
meant
oh
little one,
how tall really
your stature naturally
will always tower over
m
e
so
let

that
light
from this
packed tight
flamed bright
mind shine through goofball
eyeball lantern lenses lighting
tender
script rendered
from your tender
living
hand
and
fit
and
fashioned
just, just, just
so...
may that crazy fire's light
help you
see you,
help you
be you

follow the curve

pelican wings to carry
you
specialness
o'er the arc
of a curved world's
promises
sun-warmed wings
loft your beautiful dreams
into focus
tiny breaths
whisper where
the love is

chicago, illinois

last night
I
made a shape w/my mouth
and what dropped out?
a name of one
born
in the town of this stage
also,
my first stage
before the burden of age
anyways -
the cipher evoked
a power stroke
and kept keel
under instead of
outer so
I
could work the deck
w/crazy semaphore on
my little machine
has me
lit
lighthouse lit
foghorn fit
and the look
on those kids'
faces
making sentences

from my one word
how could they fathom
I had dreamt a whole tome
from those
nine
special
letters?

SCENE 7 FROM
SARCOXIE & SEALOVE

Sander Hicks

Originally Published: 2002

Sealove back in his dad's kitchen, Dad is eating a snack, looking at Washington Post. Ghost of Coby Benton is rummaging through the fridge.

Tom	Hi.
Sealove	Hi. What are you doing up?
Tom	I never sleep through the night any more. Where's Sarcoxie? I thought she drove.
Sealove	She did. She's spending the night at a friend's.
Tom	Someone in the band? ... How was the concert?
Sealove	The show. It was good. She has a great voice. As you know, she's grown. She's

	writing new material. I'm trying to get her to take more risks.
Tom	Ah, Risk. The soul of capitalism.
Sealove	Oh, boy. Are there any beers left (he looks for some in fridge) Risk is a myth! There is no interest in new, exciting, different forms of production in the mass media, the big money doesn't want to risk anything on substance, danger, dissent. When was the last time you tried to present a vibrant alternative to the boring status quo, and got shot up? I am risk. Capitalism hates me.
Tom	Oh, you had a small anti-establishment newspaper for a relatively short period of time. You appealed to a niche, a small, limited market, how could venture capital really find that to be scalable?
Sealove	I don't want to be in a niche! I want to liberate the masses.
Tom	But the masses want big TVs, they don't want to talk about politics.
Sealove	You're from working-class people, but when was the last time you TALKED to working-class people? You can think that, about big TVs, but you should have been there today, Hunter, the master carpenter, after the show said some incred-

ible, smart things. He knew more about politics than I thought. Working-class people are brilliant, but they are misinformed.

Tom   What about carpentry? Have you ever thought about really buckling down and getting serious about that? I mean, you're 32, you've got to be serious about something. I mean, I wouldn't mind, even if it was the carpentry. But something.

Sealove turns to Coby Benton.

Sealove   He doesn't know me.

Coby   What am I chopped liver?

Sealove *(to both)*   I can't be a carpenter all my life. I keep daydreaming of things irrelevant to building houses, and then BAM, I've driven a hammer staple through my thumbnail, I'm squealing like a girl, and cursing my thoughts. (To CB) What was your death to him?

Coby   Probably not that much of a surprise, really.

Sealove   What was your writing? What was that newspaper?

Coby   Shit, not the "crusade" you made it. But he read it in the papers when they said

97

	you were making a "crusade" about me and my writing. He loves you, Sealove, we all do. Remember that.
Tom	What about graduate school? American Literature? Then you could teach. You'd be so good.
Sealove	I know I often think about that , but in a university, I'd feel cut off from the fights of history. It's nothing without a fight. Your daughter sang that today. And now I feel better about my life. Finally.
Tom	You have no money, and at this rate, you never will. You have no savings, what if you met someone, and you wanted to settle down? It's a hell of a way to live, son, a hell of a way to live.
Sealove	How would you know? You turn on the television and sarcastically say 'let's see who we bombed today' but do you speak out against the bombing? Years ago, you said you would come with me to the counter-march protesting the Gulf War parade. But when the day came, you suddenly couldn't make it. You've got a suspicion about your own life, but then the cynicism breaks across you like a wave, and the suspicions are washed away. With a joke, or a sharp comment.

Colby	Remember, also, to say:
Sealove	I love you. But in this family, love has always been critical, an argument, a harsh assessment Hey, there's a protest against the IMF/World Bank downtown in exactly 2 weeks. Come out and join us. March. Speak out. You're of two minds, I'm talking now to the better part in you.
Tom	Those crazies? They don't know what they're talking about. They don't know economics.
Sealove	But some of your brightest colleagues have crossed the line, men you always found frank, friendly, down to earth. The world economic system needs serious repair, it needs your sober criticism. Joe Stiglitz is calling to you from the other side of the ravine. It's not easier over here, but it's better for the soul.

Tom *(while getting up)* I decided long ago that Jesus Christ didn't really rise from the dead, he was drugged by the disciples. They revived him to pull off the biggest scam in history. There are no messiahs, there is just science, and hard work. I tried to do the best I could with my life. I think I did all right. Poverty's not gone, but we put a dent in it. I'm OK with that. I think I can sleep now. *(Gets up)* I would say I love you but you make me so mad.

He exits

Ghost of Coby Benton sits where Tom was sitting

Coby	Been there, done that, got the T-shirt.
Sealove	No surprises. *(S goes to fridge for another beer.)*
Coby	We need to sleep too. You're gonna be off your schedule, partner. You're gonna be a bear to wake up at 6 on Monday.
Sealove	It's Saturday Night! Or it was.
Coby	Sleep. Dream of me. I will tell you secrets.
Sealove	You're dead. You only have the past. You're like him. I've heard the jokes a million times.
Coby	But you love them anyway. You love your old man, for his loyalty to what he believes in.
Sealove	It's become obsolete.
Coby	You have to love him because he allows you to be your own man…
Sealove	Most of the time
Coby	…And philosophize freely about a bet-

	ter world. You should tell him that sometime. He won't be around forever.
Sealove	I know
Coby	Sleep. I will tell you stories.
Sealove	But I don't want any more of your stories! That's all you are, stories! The guy at Rolling Stone wrote the story on you that's so weird now he can't get it published. He told me he can prove that you made up the Candidate's cocaine arrest story. I don't know, he won't show me the piece. Why are you such a weirdo magnet? Every month I get a new email from mysterious beings who cluck and coo how they KNOW Coby Benton didn't commit suicide, they just KNOW he got whacked by shadowy figures working for the President. I tried to get the story on you first-hand by going to your own home town in Arkansas two months after you checked out. I met the man who found your body in the hotel room with the note. He was the only cop who would really talk to me like a human being. His story held together- Credit Card fraud, alcohol abuse, massive amounts of anti-depressants, $800 cash in your pocket and a BMW in the hotel lot when you wrote, "it's time for me now to go take my pills.

Just remember, I am a good man who got caught in bad circumstances. I regret I won't walk little Adriana down the aisle some day." I'd rather crack open a beer and sit here, alone, and think with the last dying lights of sobriety, or at least awakeness, then sleep, then dream, then go somewhere with YOU, and listen to more stories.

Coby   Sealove, I thought you were the independent publisher with the balls, the stones, man, some courage. I thought you were the man. I am sorry, because I was sorely mistaken. You can believe what you want, because the note sure looked like my handwriting, didn't it? Or can they fake that? And it was written the way I write, right? Or could anyone pick up my style by reading my emails, those long winded speeches I gave you so many late nights.

It sucks being dead. I can't find new facts for you. But I can remind you of the sordid little facts you may have forgotten. My life was threatened after I survived the first media barrage. They didn't like that I was back, and that my stories would be republished in your paper. On the phone, they said, 'watch your back, watch your wife, watch little Adriana.' As easy as phoning in a bomb threat to your high school, and we've all been there, right? But I'll be damned if I didn't take it seriously. Hell, it was on my mind when I took the pills, and drank the OJ with two thirds of that litre of Smirnoff. That last night in the Days Inn, I was thinking, well, the effect is the same. Watch your back. When he said that, hell, I started to have one eye on my back all the time. It became their eye. They have an eye in my head. It could even still be here, in my ghost head.

Sealove   You're still drunk on vodka and clomazipan.

Coby   Yeah, it's great, isn't it?

Sealove   What's your point?

Coby   Well, I know you've got an event coming up.

Sealove   What event

Coby   The Big Protest

Sealove   Oh, the demo, the concert

Coby   Gonna sell a lot of newspapers?

Sealove   No, I don't run the paper any more. And I don't write any more.

Coby	Oh, right, right. But you're gonna make a big splash in the media with sis's little combo.
Sealove	I've got nothing to say to the big media. Both of their eyes have been replaced with hard boiled eggs. I would rather speak with the people in the streets.
Coby	Oh great, great, maybe you've learned. OK then, but think about this. Sarcoxie's big show, right? And you're a big help, big brother, aren't ya, gonna give the old message some more oomph, more weight, sharpen the saw, and then, well who knows what? She could be next? Would you be able to read the warning signs this time? Would you be able to guide her down better if she was too high up a tree? Are you ready to risk your family? Hell, I sure wasn't I called my lawyer, I was like, Craig, cancel the contract, but he said, Coby, we can't, the kid has the stories now and wants to go forward. Would you cancel the show if her life had been threatened? By... someone?
Sealove	You're dead. Go to bed and sleep it off.
Coby	I'm dead. But buddy I will always be with you. You become what you are not. Out of some thing comes its opposite.

Out of my death comes a new life, a new purpose for you is emerging, isn't it. Well you owe me that. You owe me your new life. I will be with you forever, my ghost will fade a little, sometimes, but then a whole new wave of suspicion will break across your brain like a drink in the face, you will wonder again how I died, and I will be alive.

[BLACKOUT]

FIVE POEMS

James Sallis

Originally Published: 2002

Second Generation

I thought of you as I drove through
the war, face turned from the train's window
beyond which lay bodies steaming from their
    wounds
in the chill of morning.
I thought how you worked to build a life
of borrowed habits, half-forgotten turns: preserves
taken from others' shelves. How you were forever
at rehearsal, trying on these new skins and masks,
trying out turns of phrase: head tilted just so,
hands held thus. How even now you go on study-
    ing
these strange people, this race, this species
among which you do not fit and will never belong.

Traveling Light

We are all guests in the language;
arrive at the border with
old schoolbooks, vaccination cards, comics
whose panels are drawn at strange angles.
How will you support yourself
while in our country? the guard asks.
Is this your first visit?
I will be earning American dollars
while here, one visitor answers. I offer
this letter of credit from my bank
in Argentina, another explains.
Once before here I have been.
These all seem to you good answers.
Now it is your turn. Words,
protect me! And if not words,
then all the possible misunderstandings.

Little Sister

This is what my life comes to, then. Ten years
of moving things from hamper to hanger
and back, excuses to your mother and mine on the
     phone,
daytime TV. And not once
did I take up your time unless I had to,
when Father died, when Lauren refused to wake
     up
in the hospital. You were always in Germany
or in seclusion, or at a meeting; your time
was important, and your life. When we spoke,
it was as though by notes
thrown between windows opened for their passage
and quickly closed, windows against which,
afterwards, I would place my hand,
finding what comfort I could in the warmth of the
     glass.

Memory

In what corner of morning
Did you encounter that horror of dawn
Breaking on the panes
When walls turned to chalk
And lights came yellow behind windows
What was it you bent
To pick up from the walk and the sea
A shell lamenting some used-up life
What have you carried home inside you
From the bank of morning

Finding Home

Now at last you can set down
the luggage of the heart.
Its place is here, after all, here
where years ago you wrote:
Bus pulls into station, my suitcase
entering first your nation,
this new content and continent.
Now at last you can unpack
the luggage of the heart,
roll up and put away
these ill-fitting clothes,
this loose second skin
too long lived in.

THE URGE TO DESTROY

Paul Tickell

Originally Published: 2002

In the film *Christie Malry's Own Double-Entry* the eponymous hero, played by Nick Moran, graduates from petty vandalism and industrial sabotage to domestic and international terrorism. He'd dearly love to do to the London skyline what the bombers of September 11 did to New York's. His world-destructive streak derives not from political extremism but from his application of the laws of accountancy to his personal life—not so much for financial gain but to avenge daily the slights and injuries visited upon him by those in authority.

For every debit there must be a credit; and tit must always be for tat in the realm of one's personal accounts. The ruthlessness with which Malry sets about balancing the books in his own favour make the black arts of the book-keepers behind Enron and Worldcom look amateurish. Whether he knows it or not, here's a man who can destroy capitalism from within by adopting its own money-grubbing logic.

Malry is a topical-sounding hero but the film was completed 18 months ago, well before Al-Qaeda terrorists and Andersen accountants tripped off the tongue. There are other prophetic elements; the film makes connections between art and terrorism, playing on the idea of the 19th century Russian anarchist Bakunin that "The urge to destroy is also the urge to create". The artist seeks to re-make the world according to his own image of it, while the terrorist does the same; however, this more desperate ape of God the Creator works in blood not paint.

The film draws parallels between Malry and Leonardo da Vinci; and now these don't seem so scandalous after the arrest a few weeks ago of an icon painter from the Greek terrorist organisation November 17. I wonder if like da Vinci Savas Xiros ever painted the face of Christ? And did he know any good accountants? Leonardo did, the best: the Franciscan monk Fra Luca Pacioli who devised double-entry book-keeping in late 15th century Italy. Such codification greased the machinery of early capitalism, when bankers were art-loving Medicis and an urban proletariat was emerging out of the Italian textile industry. Pacioli, who ghosts in and out of the film, applied the laws of mathematics to the chaos of the market-place and came up with an idea so big and simple that we don't notice it any more: debit and credit, those two columns which rule our lives, as we worry about being in the red or black.

Pacioli's colour-coding didn't stop there. Plagiarising the writings of Piero della Francesca, another painter friend, the good monk rationalised spatial chaos with another big idea, mathematical perspective. How can commerce corrupt art when since the Renaissance they've been twins anyway? Even earlier with the painter Giotto these links are visible: rather than the shepherd of popular mythology, he was a landlord capitalising on the wool-trade by renting out looms.

The poet is the antennae of the race, not the director. The topicality of the film has more to do with Simon Bent the screenwriter than me; and even more to do with the novel which we worked from. *Christie Malry's Own Double-Entry* feels like it's been written by a contemporary looking back. So it's BS Johnson who's the prophet because he wrote the book 30 years ago. He tapped into archetypal aspects of the British psyche and of early '70s London which still fascinate us, in spite of the changes of those intervening years. Is this why updating the novel and setting in 1999, the apocalyptic closing year of the millennium, wasn't such a thorny proposition?

Perhaps Johnson was ahead of his time because by 1973, the year in which *Malry* was published, he was a man out of time. Johnson was an experimental writer but not in some nancy-boy post-modernist way; he'd done National Service and been touched by the iconoclastic spirit of the '50s Angry Young Man before it turned to conservative bile. Later the openness and explosive creativity of the '60s suited the playfulness and cosmopolitan feel of much of Johnson's fiction. He looked to Europe and the Nouveau Roman and Beckett's prose (then little appreciated here compared to his plays); and to Brecht too who's quoted in *Malry*, for Johnson was a man of the left. One of the short films which he made (some of his work was cut by Bruce Beresford) was a diatribe against the union-bashing 1971 Industrial Relations Act, a Tory law which owed much to previous Labour government policy!

So the '60s dream about a cosmic alliance of workers, gays, blacks, students and holy fools was just that... Into this void crept Malry, a bank clerk and nobody but who, like some parody of '60s hedonism-cum-consumerism wants it all, loads of sex and money. He wants it now, like some prototype of *Loaded* Lad—again, no problem bringing Malry far into the 1990s, with his unashamed predilection for porn and plenty of perverse but staunchly heterosexual activity with his girlfriend. Very *Loaded* and very late '90s too is the fact that it never crosses Malry's mind that there may be other ways to improve his lot and change the world. There is no society and therefore no politics—and what are political parties but events staged by the Ministry of Sound and Fury, signifying nothing?

But the joke is that Christie becomes his own political party, a one-man anarcho-terrorist movement—a parodic composite of Angry Brigade/Baader-Meinhof Group/Red Army Fraction. By playing the system, by wanting to fit in as a consumer, while at the same time getting his own back against anybody who crosses him, Malry brings society to its knees. The novel operates like a great satiric fable, an anonymous Everyman or latterday Pilgrim whose Progress is one of selfish regress. There's a nihilism and a knockabout glee to this book which is pure punk.

Pity that Johnson, who committed suicide aged 40 at the end of 1973, couldn't have been around a little longer because punks, those ragged-arsed misanthropists proposing anarchic carnival in the UK, might have appreciated his disaffected, bitter aesthetic. Just as punk pillaged and cut up the styles of the past, so Johnson must have seemed a bit of a throwback amongst the literary ladies and gents of the early '70s. He could come over more like a porky ageing teddy boy than a writer. But at least he would have been able to relate to the punk appropriation of drapes, drain-pipes and brothel-creepers.

Underpinning the whole novel is a rage born of class. At every turn Malry comes up against the class-system and authority; but there comes the breaking-point where he stops suppurating with internal resentment and starts to make plans which the serial-killer anti-hero of *Kind Hearts and Coronets* in his one-man war against snobbery would have appreciated. Again, this aspect of Johnson's book is easily updated; in spite of all the mockney talk of classlessness and post-modernist murmurings about the End of History (supposedly because the potential for revolution putting paid to Capitalism has gone forever), we still live in an intensely class-ridden society and who's to say it can never ever be changed?

Johnson's genius was to address all kinds of ideas with robust comedy, as much *Carry On* in vein as neo-Dickensian grotesque. The scenes in the sweet-factory, where Malry works after he's sacked as a bank clerk, nail a particular English kind of servility and deference which, with a popstar 'democratic' gloss, is still very much with us if the recent Jubilee celebrations are anything to go by. This time around though there isn't the consolation of punk street-philosophers—all the more reason to adapt and update that splenetic allegory *Christie Malry's Own Double-Entry...*

MOTION THICKNESS

Guillaume Destot

Originally Published: 2002

The passage of shingly winds
on your once thin and smooth back skin
has given your spine,
now chainsawing waters and air as you zero in for
    prey,
that motion thickness.
Sand gales grate your lips
the glaze of your eyeballs scraped and dulled
by their fiercest caress
and endless rags stream behind your running
    frame
like dried liana hanging from the arms
of a Khmer God in the summer typhoon.
All curves gone angles.
All angles gone sharper still.
The very hailstones split as they meet
your razor flanks.
You now are this tempered blade,
thicker, keener, colder.

FOUR POEMS

Todd Colby

Originally Published: 2002

Iowa

Life alone creams such zones
Like a knee is gouged and no one is there.
You might take a stab at not being there.
Poultice nabbed by people on stoops,
Green glass medallion flashing in the dirt lot.
When the ring tops of bottles bare fists
The rags will later be wrapped over wounds,
Good as a rung of a ladder, my jab.
The L-step, programmed a melee
You did not have to tell a story or
nothing like that like a craving to hear a story.
Or wanting a story or even having discussed it.
I was a vandal then, marshmallows on
Windshields and such, Iowa.

From a Desk

This guy has some rooting around to do.
A spill is current, at least with the bright berry
    stains
dotting the fence around the hedges.
The children knew that the leisure puppet
had been repaired with glue made from the hooves
    of wild horses
and it frightened them. They separated themselves
    into distracted,
clownish brackets-spaced wildly.
I had not thought to brush the glass from their
    hair
so I masked my expressions of horror
with brown twine. It made my face ache. Just as
a dog will rip into a swimmer's face, so my big
    bummer
has sprung into different parts. The ruthlessness
of the intern, career-wise, all the misery foretold.
I locked arms with a witless celebrant, being the
    gloomy one-
always racing the animals, competing with them in
    a pool
until they can't take it anymore—until they give up
    hope.

Arnica

To be calm
is to be comfortably
moist at the hip. My tongue
is shaped like something sucked
from a shell. My sparks are still good,
I shed them in the golden light
of 8th Avenue all the way
across town where the cab drivers veer toward me.
Brisk doors whoosh past all the guys from Tech
School. They see me with steel eyes
and stand up to the sound of a skidding car.
I don't care
if you don't have
a care in the world-
you see me and I see
the day is not-so-quietly exploding
while Mercury humps mythical pudding into blue
    smoke.
I'll sit right down in Gramercy Park on that fenced
    off patch of
silvery
grass.
I had my photo taken there once and never got it
    back.
There's a part of me that twinkles like slivers of
    glass
embedded in the sidewalk and another part that I
    have to read about

in magazines to get a grip on what the fuck I'm up
    to. Clipped
and sordid, I bake in the sunlight and sculpt
sexy shapes from the granite we're built on.
I've explained my problem
with my leg in the air and I can't get
anyone to act like that.
Still, the pieces of me; they glitter,
sort of, it's this glass, I'm real.
Don't let me distract you
with this tincture for bruises-
maybe I should, you know,
stop. Calm as the everglades,
I'm not so sure.

Squash Buckler

Noble one of simmer mode
The hankie is pulverized
By the wedge of sports
A vehicle of downers
A drowsy stagehand
Magnificent oranges
All the wedding cake you
Can eat a handful
At a time.

CURED

Jim Martin

Originally Published: 2002

Dinner was just finishing up when the doorbell rang. Angela had been making preparations for this meal all week, and it was finally happening. Outside the door stood her one-time lover, Darryl. They had been together for just a little more than a year, but the relationship had been a rocky one. The relationship had been defined quite nicely by the way the two of them had first met.

They were at a house party, nearly 300 people showing up at what should have been a birthday party for a kid that Darryl knew from school. Angela had come with a friend of hers who was meeting her boyfriend. The party was the sort of wild nightmare that most parents fear; there were holes in walls, underaged kids drinking and using drugs, and people having sex in any room with a door on it. Darryl had entered the bathroom to piss only to find Angela half-asleep in the bathtub. A few choice words later, and the two were naked. A pathetic few moments later, and the two were clothed again. In that little exchange, Little Elle was conceived. When Angela found out, she had to ask around to find out the name of the man who had fathered her child.

To his credit, Darryl tried his hardest to do right by her. The two started dating, and he did his best to try to help her with the pregnancy. When he turned 18, he dropped out of school and got a job on the same construction site his father worked at so he could move out and live with Angela. Naturally, things didn't work out. Darryl liked to drink, and often came home drunk and angry. No matter how hard he tried, he just seemed incapable of staying sober, and eventually Angela knew that she had to break it off.

That was all over now. Angela finally had a firm plan in place, a plan that started with this dinner. She had baked lasagna and toasted up some garlic bread, set the table with the good dishes her mother had bought her, and lit a candle. Sitting on the table was a cold beer, something she knew he would appreciate and that would set the mood for the evening.

Darryl entered holding flowers for her. He seemed legitimate in his desire to make things better. They exchanged some small talk, then sat down to dinner. The baby was upstairs asleep, and the quiet of the house added just the right sizzle to the mood.

Throughout dinner, the two talked. Angela wanted Darryl to know how much she loved him and missed him. Darryl wanted to tell Angela about how he was ready to go to counselling, how he really wanted to be a part of the baby's life, and how he really wanted to be with Angela. Angela giggled and blushed.

The conversation became flirtatious.

Then naughty.

Then blatant.

She told him to go upstairs and get ready. She told him she wanted to be close to him. She told him she wanted him. He rose with a wicked grin and moved towards the stairway, one of those cheap staircases with white painted metal railings. When he was a few steps up, she pulled out the gun and put two bullets in his back. The first was the calculated strike, the second an almost accidental reaction to the surprise she felt at the incredible noise the first had made. She dropped the gun, stunned.

When the police arrived, the house was a mess. They found the woman who had called the police sitting in obvious shock on the carpet near the phone. There was a child upstairs howling that she didn't seem to hear. The dinner was spilt on the floor, there were signs of a struggle, and there was the body on the stairs. Angela told them how she had tried to patch things up with him for the sake of the child. He had come over for dinner. They were just talking, sort of feeling out the waters, and then all of the sudden he started talking like they were back together again. She told him that she couldn't do it any more, that they didn't work. He became angry. He had been drinking.

He started yelling. He hit her. He threw the tray of food on the ground and started screaming at her. He told her he was going to go take what was his, and he started walking up the stairs calling her daughter. The next thing she knew, he was dead, and she just broke down. She didn't even remember calling the police.

Two years later, Angela got to leave the mental hospital and return home. Society understood things. She had been the victim. She had acted terribly, but in that awful sort of way that we all know lies inside of us all. She was a mother protecting her young. She was punished, but she learned her lesson, and her doctors were saying she had made some impressive steps in their care. She wasn't a danger to anyone else. She was cured.

FETISH ALPHABET

Susannah Breslin

Originally Published: 2002

A is for Anthropophagy

He was an anthropophagiac, and so he could never understand why, if other people could, say, eat green eggs and ham, why then could he not eat a woman if he so wanted? He shook his head back and forth as he sat in his armchair in his living room. The men that he saw out in the world every day wanted to eat women, and he knew this because he watched them chew at women's faces in big mouthfuls, and grab handfuls of women's buttocks, and as they did it say, Yummm, and, Mmmmm. The women, for their part, he knew they wanted to be eaten because he saw them on his TV-screen longing to be devoured and consumed and taken in every piece of themselves, and it was in their eyes and the hike of their skirts and the way they rolled their tongues around in their mouths.

But, instead of doing what he so wanted, he sat here by himself every night, holding a bucket of chicken wings dowsed in ketchup with his imagination working harder than his stomach. It was ridiculous, he thought, a tear coming to the edge of his lonely eye. America is not beautiful, really, he saw now. He bit down on another skinny chicken leg in the blue bask of his TV-screen, and he wondered, why is it so hard in this world for a man to eat a woman?

B is for Bestiality

Things had, of course, started down on the farm. In the distance rolled the endless green hills, in the barn swelled mounds of yellow straw. Each day, before the rabbit's cage, a young boy would come to stand, sticking his fingers in through the holes of the bunny's small enclosure. Each night, the boy would return, taking the rabbit off into the dark trees listing at the end of the farm's undulating grasses. It was not until, as a teenager, flipping through the pages of a magazine, that the boy found a new kind of rabbit to love. This one took the form of a naked woman in a pink see-through bunny suit, her boobs and butt curving out towards him from underneath her flopping bunny ears. His hand, meanwhile, had crawled like a speeding crab right down to his shorts. Decades later, when the boy had become a man, who had married and divorced and had a great many women, he had engineered his whole life so that rabbits were all around him now at all times. And yet, what he had found was that no matter how many buildings he built, or how many bunnies he humped, none of them could ever take the place of that old rabbit down on the farm. Finally, when he had, at last, become a very old man, and lay dying on his deathbed with his mouth drawn into a wide-open cry, outside of his bedroom door waited only a herd of blonde bunnies. And, yes, they whispered to each other, his last wish really had, in fact, been for rarebit. And, indeed, they cooed, in the end, he had actually died with his broken hips thrusting into what every single one of them hoped was some kind of rabbit paradise.

C is for Conjoined Twins

You had to love them, he thought, for how could you not, for you could not hate them, could you? There were so many things about them, after all, to love.

Take, for example, when he was having them both—for how could he not?—as the likelihood one of them would be moaning, even if the other was yawning her mouth or rolling her eyes, was still incredibly high. If one went along, the other one had to; this was the beauty of their Y-shape in God's own design. Now, whether or not the two of them needed him at all—this was the thought that woke him up screaming into the night as they lay sleeping side-by-side beside him.

He knew it was entirely possible that one day they would stop bickering and fighting and putting their fingers into each other's eyes, and he would be the one underneath them while one of them held his hands and the other one sliced his tongue in two with his own steak knife. Their two noodles sat suspended in divided vessels above undivided bodies, but to what degree they ever truly worked apart was nature's greatest mystery.

Thank god, he thought, as he pushed the lawn-mower past the window where the two of them were now standing with a hand on each hip, staring down at him through their four narrowed eyes as the wet grass sprayed up and across his face in the terrible summer heat once again. Thank god that I hold the key to their lock between my legs, and praise the Lord that I am the pile-driver of their undivining love for me.

D is for Dachryphilia

You never truly knew what you were getting into on the day that you were born, now did you?, she thought to herself. For here she was today, her hands shaped in two cups, as the girl's insides tumbled into her palms. Surely, he had meant well with this gift for her of the anatomical doll who had arrived in a box marked SWEET SUE. But, when she had removed the female figurine's breastplate all its insides had come falling out, and then, Oh, oh!, Milton had cried, grappling into the empty air with his fat, white, and pasty hands. It was too late. By the time Sweet Sue's small lungs had toppled, and her dark slab of kidney had fallen, and her plastic heart sat woodenly up on top of it all, Darlene, for all intents and purposes, had already left the scene of the crime. Inside her mind, it was as if reality was only a chalk outline drawn around a blood-soaked body that had been gurneyed away to the morgue. She had gone back in her head to that moment in time at which she had stood across from the young boy down by the lake near her child-hood home, envisioning gutting him like a fish out of water, as he had systematically eviscerated her with his small, pink, and narrow tongue. So, today, while, thankfully, he was no longer alive, having drowned himself many years ago in his own bathtub, as his wife had washed the dishes, even though the pieces of Sweet Sue were bone cold to the touch, Darlene could hardly wait to feel Milton's heart beating hot and wet between her two hands as she squeezed out of him the sorry tears of his all too easily won love for her.

E is for Eunuch

You could call him nullified, or orchidectomized, or emasculated, or a eunuch, but he was simply the pos-sessor of a penectomy, a person who no longer bore his penis, a man undeniably lacking in what he had previously carried in his lower basket, and he had, therefore, since become the ingestor of a multitude of hormone-filled pharmaceuticals, and turned into the personal curator of his own Johnson in a jar, and resultingly realized that he was now the type of individual who could silence an entire dinner-party full of people at the mere drop of a hat with the mere drop of his pants, and yet what he had discovered since this rather sudden change of life events was that while he had fantasized rapturously as a young man of chemical castration, and spent several years seriously considering moving to India to linger amongst the third-sexed there by the banks of the Katni River, it was actually only one year ago that his brain had become wholly overrun by words like "Elastrator," and "Burdizzo," and "Underground Doctors," and it was only rather recently that he had found himself lying quite awake, because he had wanted it that way, on a cold kitchen table, because they had wanted it that way, praying to whomever looked over poor souls like him that someday someone would lean over him in some dark bed somewhere and be happy to find him so wonderfully smooth, but the problem was that now, today, at this very moment, in that imaginary bed he was truly lying, and he knew without a doubt, even with the lights off, that the person lying next to him was doing nothing but snoring, and coming down the back alleyways of his mind for him was his own terrible penis, and it was angry, and it was carrying at its side an entire suitcase filled to overflowing with his whole, long, lonely life that he had lived thus far, and, already, the suitcase was falling open and spilling its whole horrible mess out all over the floor of his mind, and he knew, with no reservations needed, thank you very much, that he would slip in it, and that this new smoothness of his, which had been intended to lubricate his life, would make it impossible for him to ever get back up again.

F is for Forniphilia

She was standing in the corner. She had a lampshade on her head. The lampshade was making her head sweat. *I am a lamp*, she told herself. She was standing in the corner with her arms straight down at her sides and a lampshade on her head, waiting for her husband to come home. Her husband wanted her to be a lamp. Her husband was great. But he wanted his wife to be different pieces of furniture, depending on the day of the week. That was hard. For her. It turned him on. She said out loud, "I am a lamp". She didn't really want to be a lamp, though. She wanted to be a human being. That was the problem. *A lamp*, she told herself. *I am a lamp*, she thought again. Who knew what she would be tomorrow? Maybe she would become an armchair. *An armchair is better than a lamp*, she told herself. But then it occurred to her that being an armchair would probably require her to bend both of her legs all the way back over her head so that her butt would become the seat. And that wouldn't be comfortable. At all. Then god only knew what would happen if her husband wanted to sit down on top of her at his desk to do some work that he had brought home from the office. Probably, she would break. A broken armchair. She heard her husband's key as it began to turn in the lock of their front door. She thought to herself, *At this rate, I will end up as a bike rack.* Day in and day out, she imagined in her mind's eye for herself, she would ride around on the back of her husband's car. In the wind. In the rain. In the snow. It would never end. The tall dark outline of her husband stepped into the room. *I am a lamp*, she told herself underneath the lampshade. That was what her husband wanted. She turned herself on.

I WAS A TEENAGED GO-GO GIRL

Charlotte Cooper

Originally Published: 2003

Do you know what a go-go girl is?

Go-go girls are the hottest bitches on the scene, they're the queens of the night. When you see them twitching their thighs and shaking it, it makes you want to shout out Go Baby Go! Go Baby Go! as you wipe nervous randy sweat from your forehead with a spotted hankie.

Where did go-go girls come from? I guess it's something to do with the Whisky A Go Go club in LA that was so popular with those hip-swinging 60s folk back before flower power ruined everything.

Go-go girls wear white make-up and little white kinky boots. They have big big hair and little little dresses. They are either very sullen or very smiley. Their boyfriends are bouncers at the clubs where they work. They spend a lot of time fighting off frisky admirers. Go-go girls do dances with names: the Shimmy, the

Swim, the Watusi. Sometimes they get put in a cage or on a podium, they are the chosen people after all. They love to dance and dance and dance and dance, and they get paid for it too.

Go-go fact: Go-go girls who don't make it end up as strippers and they often become lesbians. Another go-go fact: Go-go girls often have acne-scarred skin.

Anyway, that's a little lesson in go-go-ology.

Lemme tell you, I've been dining out on this story for quite a while. I would like people to think that I often do cool things, and that my life is a testament to coolness in every way, that I don't really like Simon and Garfunkel, or have a verruca, or wear big pants from chubby lady shops. But the truth is that what I am going to tell you about my short career as a teen-aged go-go girl stands out as the coolest thing I've ever done. It's one of those stories that goes in and out of fashion. During the late eighties and most of the nineties, nobody gave a shit when I told it, but now that the whole NY punk thing is big again, I've got a whole new audience to boast at.

Okay, so here goes. In 1986 I was working as the Saturday girl at the Spastics Society charity shop in Wembley. This entailed: being surly to customers, smoking Silk Cut all day long, taking money, bitching and complaining incessantly, getting things out of the window display for people to paw and prod, refusing to haggle, having the first pick of the donations, stealing money from the collections tin, and being in love with my teen colleague Mick. (Michael Taylor of

Wood Green, if you are out there I still burn a flame for you.)

The manager of the shop's boyfriend used to be in a very successful punk band but had fallen on hard times. They both knew a lot of people from the seventies punk scene in London. Leee Black Childers was one of their friends who used to drop by now and again. Leee used to manage David Bowie, Iggy and the Stooges, the Heartbreakers, lots of people. One of his best friends was Jayne County.

Now some of you might be too young or too square to know who Jayne is. I'll fill you in. Jayne was born in the deep south in the fifties. Back then she was called Wayne. She moved to New York City and lived with Jackie Curtis and a whole load of other Warhol drag queens and she starred in his play, *Pork*. Jayne was not a drag queen, she is a transgendered woman. She had a couple of bands and became a rock'n'roll star. One of her most famous songs goes: "If you don't want to fuck me baby, baby fuck off!" She's recorded it ten times, including a hi-NRG version. Jayne became a scene face during the punk years, she was a regular at CBGBs. She had a dress made of wigs. In the eighties she moved to Berlin and had some surgery. She came to London, which is where I met her.

Jayne fact: the city of Detroit stands in an area called Wayne County—any connection to Jayne? Who knows!

My boss and her boyfriend treated me like some kind of protege. It was a weird friendship. They used to take me out to clubs with them, terrible mid-eighties places, Rusty Egan type places. The Wag Club.

Leee's friend Angie Bowie was in town doing some shows with Mick Ronson, so we went to see her. I wore, as always, one of my vintage fifties ballgowns purloined from the Spastics Society. Jayne was there, she came up and said how much she liked my frock. I guess she'd been eyeing me up. Not long after that, my boss said that Jayne was looking for a fat go-go dancer and would I like to do it?

Would I? Would I? Would I? Fuck yeah!

A week later, Jayne met me at Brixton Station, we took a bus together to her flat in Streatham. She told me the plan: there would be two go-go girls, one fat, one thin—comic genius, right? We would wear nylon babydoll negligees (which were ten a penny in charity shops in those days) and dance around on stage during Jayne's forthcoming show at ... oh my god... Peter Stringfellow's eighties superclub, the Hippodrome!

Jayne had already lined up a skinny girl, a model, this really hip young rich thing, but she soon abandoned the idea and I was kind of relieved. I roped in a girl I knew from college, this awkward goth kid, a bona fide anorexic too. To my shame I can't remember her name.

Our rehearsals consisted of sitting around Jayne's front room and watching John Waters videos. Jayne narrated the first 50 minutes of Female Trouble to me one time, she knew it so well. I thought it was a film about her life.

Another time, me and the anorexic went and ate at the Pizza Hut opposite Jayne's place. I mean 'ate' in the loosest terms because my ana pal merely pushed her food around the plate, she was living mostly on vitamin pills at that stage. I looked up towards Jayne's flat and saw her silhouetted in the window, like Norman Bates at the Psycho mansion. She waved and we waved back.

Showday arrived. We had our own dressing room, a proper lights round the mirror deal, and our tiny window looked out over a brothel, each room was illuminated by a red lightbulb. We got into our outfits and sat around, bored. Showbusiness was not as exciting as we'd been led to believe. Jayne came and gave us a nip of sulphate, a tiny dab off the end of a key. More waiting. More waiting. More waiting. Then... action!

Someone took us to the stage through the back of the building, all winding corridors, narrow doorways, pipes and fuseboxes. The Hippodrome had a hydraulic stage that came up out of the floor, we took our places on the platform, ready to be elevated up into the main dance area. It's funny, these are the memories that remain with me so much more clearly than the actual show itself.

The audience consisted of tourists, goths, ageing punks, assorted gayboys, club kids and the trendiest girl from college alongside her closeted best friend. She couldn't believe that we were dancing around, she had no idea that me and the anorexic girl could possibly have this cool secret life that she knew nothing about. We rubbed her nose in it, for sure, we shimmied on the stage right over her and openly sneered in her face.

Jayne sang along to a backing tape, what?, four or five songs. "Cream in My Jeans", "Fuck Off". Some others. The anorexic girl and I danced around, shaking our arses at the audience, showing our knickers, being totally unafraid, free, the coolest kids in the world, absolutely triumphant! Then we disappeared down into the depths of the club on that stupid fucking stage. It was over pretty quickly.

So that was it. There were plans to repeat the show, but they never took off. I'd see Jayne now and again, but I was too young really to be a proper friend, and she was part of my boss's crowd, not mine. I don't know if she would remember me now.

My Mum was dying of breast cancer when I was a go-go girl for the legendary punk outlaw transsexual and all-round heroine Jayne County, in fact Mum died shortly afterwards. With her death my life changed, it sobered everything, it froze me. Things became still for a while.

AFTERNOON PLAY

Tony White

Originally Published: 2003

'What's wrong, Hugh? Are you going to tell me?'

Tom is looking out of the window through the nets while speaking, eyelids flickering slightly as his gaze moves from the brick barbecue at the edge of the patio, over the pond, to the hammock which is slung between two trees beyond the kitchen extension to the left.

'You've been like this all day.' *All bloody year, more like.*

The eucalyptuses are wildly out of proportion to the rest of the garden. *Bloody trees.* The grass needs cutting, and the pond which the two of them dug that first summer in the house is a seething mass of life. For a second or two he watches the afternoon light reflected on its boiling surface.

'Bloody frogs. Thought they always went back to where they were born when they fancied a shag.' He smiles to himself. 'Someone must have told a little porkie once upon a time.'

'What? Oh. Yes.' A half-smile briefly flickers across Hugh's face. He's sitting in the Eames chair with his slippered feet on the matching foot stool. 'Where's that heron when we need him, eh, Tom? That's what I'd like to know.'

Looking down to admire the antique olive jars against the York stone, Tom encounters a patch of condensation on the glass instead. *Been standing here too long*, he thinks, then notices the thin, fractally-ragged line of darker something or other between the cold glass and the metal frame, and the smell of smoke in the nets. *Good taste, that's all, and I can't say I blame him. Which would you take, given the choice, eh? Koi Carp or a bloody frog?*

Turning, he opens his mouth and draws breath as if he's just about to say something but by the time his eyes have adjusted to the darkness of the room, he sees that the twinkle in Hugh's eye has gone and he thinks better of it: 'Don't try and change the bloody subject.'

'I wasn't, hun. It was you that mentioned frogs.'

Tom takes his hands out of the pockets of his Levis and walks the few steps from the window to the door. 'Let's have a bit of light shall we,' he says, flicking the switch. 'Are you listening to that?'

'I was.'

'Oh. She was. And I suppose I'm bloody interrupting.'

Yes. 'No, of course not, babe. I just forgot to turn it off.'

'Can't we have some music on for a change? Bloody Afternoon Play. I don't know how you can listen to that shit, sweetie.'

I like it. 'I had it on for the news. That's all.' The leather creaks as he sits up and swings his feet off of the foot stool. He swivels and leans over to take a packet of Dunhill from the bed-sized, oval marble table in the centre of the room. He lights one with a Bic which he replaces in his cardigan pocket, then, blowing out the smoke he reaches across to an ashtray which he rakes across the marble with two fingers until it's a comfortable arm's length away. Sitting up a bit straighter he takes a drag.

'Anyway, you said you didn't want to come.'

Hugh says nothing, takes another drag, then watches the blue smoke curling from the tip of his cigarette.

'Hugh?'

He looks up.

'I wouldn't have gone if I'd thought you didn't want me to.'

'Don't be silly, hun. You know I don't mind you going out.'

Hugh gently slides the cigarette back and forth along the rim of the ashtray, until the first tiny flake of ash falls off. Tom touches the radiator which runs along the wall beneath the window.

'Bloody heating's not on.'

'Mm?'

'Freezing in here.' He considers quoting Pynchon—
'vuh-vuh-vuh' on the inhale—like they used to when
they went to bed on cold nights. But he doesn't.

'Put a jumper on, then. What do you expect, walking around in a T-shirt in March?'

'Aren't you cold? Oh, bugger it,' Tom says, walking
to the fireplace and fiddling with the ignition button; wincing as the basket of fake coal goes on with a
whoomp of blue flame. Hands on knees he stands up
then presses the 'off' button on top of the Roberts on
the mantelpiece. Rubbing his upper arms in turn, he
walks around the marble slab to the side of the room
opposite the fire place and reaches up under the shade
of an Art Deco standard lamp. Behind it, the wall is
lined with the bookshelves which he stopped noticing years ago. He glances at the poster for *Passport to
Pimlico* that hangs on the wall behind the Eames. The
blue signature scrawled across Stanley Holloway's face
is illegible. Not even Holloway's—just some bit-part
bitch Hugh claimed to have slept with. He wonders
why he once loved it, why he once loved the whole
of this man's sprawling personal mythology. Studied
it like his life depended on it. Perhaps it did, once.
He adjusts the cushion on one of a pair of identically
upholstered chaise longues which are set on either
side of the lamp. Sitting down, he runs his fingers
through cropped salt and pepper hair.

'You said you didn't want to come,' he says, brush-
ing some fluff from his Levis. 'I really didn't think it'd
bother you, that's all.'

Hugh takes a last drag then extinguishes his cigarette with a series of stabbing movements. Puts the ashtray on the foot stool, then puts it back on the table.

'For Christ's sake, Tom. Stop going on about it, will you?'

Shocked slightly by the volume of his own voice he sits back a little. Elbows on the chair arms and palms together, he rests his chin on his thumbs and looks at the ornamental cigarette lighter in the centre of the slab, noticing the way that the light from the window reflects on the surface of the marble, and the rings left by two glasses where it doesn't.

Tom stands up. 'Keep your hair on.'

'What time did you get back?'

Tom sits down again. 'I don't know. Must've been after one I suppose. You were asleep, babe.'

Three, thinks Hugh. *Couldn't*. He rolls his eyes and begins to sigh, then stops himself.

'I hate it when you do that.'

'I know, hun. Sorry.'

'I didn't want to wake you, that's all.'

Hugh wishes that the radio was still on. Something to fill the gaps.

'Who was there?' he asks without looking up.

'Oh, that's it, is it?' Tom sneers without meaning to. Gets him into trouble sometimes. Like Hugh's 'tut-tuts', it used to be ironic and highly endearing. Used to be. It goes un-noticed this time.

Hugh's arm has stopped half-way to the cigarettes. He looks up. 'Of course that's not "it". There is no bloody "it".'

'Can't fool me, sweetie. Wish you'd tell me what's wrong.'

Hugh is suddenly aware that he's slightly smaller than he once was. He looks at the brown spots on the backs of his hands, then picks up the packet and takes one out. 'There's nothing bloody wrong, Tom. Do stop going on, love.' Fiddles for his Bic.

'She was there as a matter of fact. Since you ask.'

Fag in mouth. *Did I?* Hugh thinks, but says, 'Mmhmm. How is she?'

'Don't be like that. Nothing ever bloody happened, I've told you.'

Told me something, thinks Hugh, remembering. *But I know it wasn't the half of it.* He wants to smile, but gloating's Tom's game. *You're too bloody old now anyway*, he thinks. *He wouldn't touch you with a bloody barge pole and you know it.*

'Hardly spoke to her all night as a matter of fact. Centre of attention as usual. Knocking it back.'

I bet she was, thinks Hugh. *Stupid little tart.* 'Works hard at it, though, Tom. You've got to give the bastard that.'

'Anna couldn't get enough of it, of course. Bless.'

'Anna was there? Anna Haycraft?'

'That's what I said, darling. Couldn't believe my eyes, I can tell you.'

'How is she?'

'On good form, actually. Going back to the convent.'

'She always says that.'

'That's what I said, but she said she means it this time.'

'She always says that, too.'

They smile at each other for a second.

Tom leans back on the chaise longue, and rests an ankle on his knee. 'Sinclair told her Mike's Portobello story. Footballs over the convent wall, you know.' He picks at a loose thread on the side of his loafer then brushes off some imaginary dirt with the tips of his fingers.

I told you that story. 'Bet she enjoyed that.'

'Oh, yes. Of course she did. Never played football herself, but says they had the best time. Said she never giggled so much in her life. Her eyes lit up when he mentioned Mike.'

'I didn't know they...'

'Knew each other? Well, who knows, but it's a small world now, so you can imagine what it was like then, sweetheart.'

As if I wasn't there, Hugh thinks, forcing a smile.

'Some pissed diarist came over. Ignored me completely, the stupid bitch. Things I could tell you, sweetie, I thought. He's doing another film.'

Just as easy to get lost then. Thought it bloody was, anyway. 'Oh? Who?'

'Sinclair, of course. Asked after you, darling. Oh, don't worry. I painted a pretty picture. Working hard, I said. In our little Hertfordshire bloody idyll.'

Stubbing out his cigarette. 'Who's he making a film about?'

'Mike. That's when Anna's eyes lit up. Said they used to call him "More and more and more..."'

'Yes, I remember.'

'I said he should come and see us if he's passing. Pop in for a cup of tea and a fondant fancy.'

'Mike? I thought he was…'

'Sinclair.'

'Oh!' Hugh practically leaps out of his chair. 'For crying out loud, what did you go and do that for! He will now. Hope you didn't say I was writing something. Jesus bloody Christ! He'll ask me how it's going and I'll have to pretend to be in the middle of it. Jesus, Tom! He's writing about the M25 these days, for Christ's sake. Be knocking at the door with a bloody camera crew next, asking about the old days. Trying to connect me to some bloody conspiracy or other. And that's all I need.'

'Well, listen to her! Pardon me for breathing, I'm sure.'

'Another bloody hatchet job. Jesus, Tom. Why?'

'Thought you'd like the attention, pumpkin.' Tom cocks his head to one side, and does his sympathetic mother voice, shaking his head a little as he speaks. 'Tom only wants what's best for you, sweetie. Everyone's asking when you're going to do something. Take a bit of credit for a change. For Christ's sake, you could do a little Afternoon Play.'

God forbid. Hugh jumps at a barely audible noise. Then the phone begins to ring. Jesus.

'Expecting someone?'

Of course. 'Hardly.'

'No, no. You sit there. I'll get it.'

Tom stands up and walks to an occasional table near the door. He picks up the handset, simultaneously aligning the phone and the edge of the Salisbury Cathedral place mat that it stands on with his other hand.

'Hello.'

They won't answer. Not to you.

'Hello?'

It's not you they want, you bloody fool.

'No-one there.' He hangs up. 'Drink?'

That won't help. 'Lovely.'

Tom walks through to the kitchen. He reaches into the cupboard next to the sink to flick the switch on the thermostat, then closes the door and bends to open the dishwasher.

Listening to the sound of the kitchen drawer being opened, the dull rattle of cutlery, and the cork being pulled, Hugh wonders when they're going to stop calling, but hopes in a way that they don't, because when they stop calling is when they'll start knocking on the door, and that would be infinitely worse than the silences on the line or, as happened last night, that damnable voice from, what, thirty-five, forty years ago. 'Hello, Hughie old son,' he'd said. Hugh winces as he remembers his eventual, faltering 'I'm afraid you must have the wrong number,' and the laugh which greeted this pathetically transparent lie. He'd thrown the handset down as if a cockroach had crawled out of it. As if? One had.

'Well it's not exactly the cocktail hour, but I've opened one of the good ones.' Tom enters the room, opening and closing the door with his right foot. The wine and two glasses are on a black and gold lacquer tray which he sets down on the marble table, grunting involuntarily as he straightens back up for a second. He looks down at Hugh then bends to pick up the bottle and pour two generous glasses full.

'Lovely,' Hugh nods, aware that his slightly pained smile has something of the martyr about it. He hadn't meant it to. It was just how it came out. He hopes Tom missed it. That kind of thing drives him up the wall.

Tom hands him a glass. 'That's three times in the last week,' he says, picking up his own, 'Joke's wearing a bit thin now isn't it, darling.' Tom perches on the foot stool and takes a sip of wine.

It's not a bloody joke. Wish it were. Hugh takes a too-large swig, but then stops himself downing it like a cold beer. He realises that he can't swallow the whole mouthful all at once, and sits there trying not to choke or spit it out. It's making his eyes water but he manages it. He puts the glass on the table and takes another Dunhill from the packet, aware that his hand is shaking slightly.

'Kids, probably.' says Tom, knowing that if it was kids there'd be lots of them giggling before one of them plucked up the courage to shout 'Batty!'

'Yes, probably,' says Hugh, trying to sound unconcerned.

'Same ones that have been chucking sweet wrappers over the hedge.'

Hugh can't help being relieved that he's swallowed his wine. 'What do you mean?' *Don't overdo it, Hugh. Bit too shrill.*

'Mars bars, Curly Wurly, Boost. You'd think this was the way home from the bloody Cadbury's factory.'

Coincidence, surely, please God. 'When was this?'

'Oh, only every day this week, but never you mind I'll take care of the garden.'

Hugh feels the room swimming, and starts to take a deep breath, but realises that it would be taken for a comment on Tom's regular rant about dereliction of gardening duty. He half glances up, but Tom is looking over towards the phone.

'Wouldn't be someone for you would it, hun?'

'No. What? The...'

'Some old flame? I don't know. You're a dark horse you are.'

'You know there's only ever been you, Tom. You're the only man for me. You know that.' Hugh taps his cigarette on the ashtray, confident in the truth of what he's saying, and hoping that this truth will paper over the larger lie. 'You do know that, don't you?'

They both sit in silence for a while, Hugh smoking, Tom taking the occasional sip of wine, both wishing that the radio was still on but not wanting to be the one who admits their guilt by doing so.

Tom speaks first. 'You're not seeing someone else are you, sweetie?'

'Oh for Heaven's sake, Tom! Of course I'm not! Where on Earth did that come from? We're together all the time, darling.'

Not last night though, Tom thinks. *No wonder you were so bloody eager to send me off.* 'Bit of a classic though, don't you think? Silences on the line when the wrong one answers the phone.'

'Classic? Christ, it'll have its own song in Diana: the Musical,' says Hugh, smiling and exhaling at the same time, the laugh turning into a slight cough which is silenced by a quick clear of the throat.

Tom laughs. 'Every other bloody song'll involve telephones.'

'In the third act they will,' says Hugh, aware of a lingering thickness in his voice. He clears his throat again.

They've cast and re-cast this stage show. It's become a fantasy vehicle for every damaged showbiz personality they can think of. Tom remembers casting Dorothy Squires as Camilla Parker-Bowles last time they played, but his knowledge was gleaned solely from Hugh's LP collection, and the suggestion was dismissed with a shake of the head. 'She'd make a better Queen Mum,' Hugh had said, 'If she were still alive'. 'Wouldn't have thought that would matter,' Tom had said. 'They could just wheel around the corpse. No-one'd notice.'

They both smile at each other for a second, then Tom takes a sip of wine and looks at the mantelpiece.

'Play's probably finished,' he offers, putting his left

hand on Hugh's knee.

Hugh transfers his cigarette from right to left, then lays his hand briefly on top of Tom's. Too briefly. More like a pat. *Damn. The gesture of a distracted nurse*, he thinks, registering the slight tightening of Tom's jaw and deciding, quickly, to bring that hand to his mouth as if he were about to cough again, as if the withdrawal of his hand had been some sort of politeness reflex. Clearing his throat unnecessarily, he waits for the moment when he can replace his hand on Tom's. 'How about some music, instead?' he asks.

'Not in the mood now,' says Tom. *You never were any good at lying*, he thinks, taking his hand away before Hugh can follow through.

'Anyone else there?' asks Hugh, in an effort to restore the moment.

Tom drains his glass in one go, and stands up. 'No-one you'd know, darling.'

THREE POEMS

Travis Jeppesen

Originally Published: 2003

Mountain of Yearning

A fine rash establishes itself on my torso. Another
yellow morning to get lost in. The day will become the adventure of ants in a cage, burying
their way towards oxygen. All they'll find is a
black man's skull. I don't want to stay official on
that one. Wish our leaders made us docile. But
instead, we're merely allowed.

Leaning toward booger venture. Plastic explosion,
the newsman. Ugliest actor still has to find work.
Subtle us some more, I love you. Moses deep
inside. We shade the raid. He who must kick
down the door. A lone rat is your honest answer.
We must learn to invent sideways dimension.
Smashed E on the walkway, a thin bridge leads
us there. No one knows. The truth a bee sting.

Eat My Rot, Corky

A new kind of chewing gum can satisfy
all tastes. It's amazing, the stuff
they come up with these days. It makes
me glad I'm not allergic to the sun.
There are worse things, I imagine, but
we're not interested in entering them in
our limited vocabulary. The trees offer
too much comfort. We see the open
frontier, but when we reach out to
touch it, find it flat and staticy.
The hair stands up on the back of our
necks. Just looking doesn't cause
that. Guess you have to defamiliarize
yourself with something before you
second-guess it.

Last Poem

Eat logic hot dog bugger. Magic
stain octagon name black skulls
push a button. Not to "variance" the
shock, but to allergic psychosomatic
suffusion lack time sphere demonic
Italy. Runty surety palm fore, knots
in cots also black. Transpire the
Microphone face lawyer. Time spinner
block stem. Hawks, cats knock over
the hot iron steam. TV Grandma,
everyone's gay in the USA. Beard
and toenail trimmers unite against
the threat of fascism, world is
saved. So we find another leader
To pick apart like vultures in a
humidifier. Who wants to be a millionaire?
That guy's tie. To personify numbers
is all that's left. We cannot come
down to the level that's been forced,
we are left vulnerable to hallucinated
existence instead. Let's kill gravity,
Invent another system to defy, see-
through being will float like olives
in a martini, graced with the over-
whelming fact of presence in all
its undiluted forms (if there are
any left.) Just to stand there
naked would be enough, but we

have to fuck things up with the
wind in order to give voice to
all the appliances we keep around
us, as though they'll protect us
from whatever invading force
we've invented to keep us clean. It's
abstract, the illusion of wildfires,
devouring the cities we've worked
so hard to build to destroy.
Skiing down a woman's breast becomes the last thing we can hope
for, that and the ingrained desire
that we'll awaken tomorrow
morning with nothing left to say.

YEAH I FUCKED YOU

Jeri Cain Rossi

Originally Published: 2003

John Doe 49
Denver, CO 1985

Should I be a madonna or a whore? I wondered as I
rode around Denver in the ice and storm with you, an
American Icon Rock Star Poet Warrior of the People.
But you had no such hang-ups as you pushed my
head into your lap on Colfax Ave. Not wanting to be
recognized you paid for a motel room under an alias.
And as I sat on top I asked you who you really were
even though I was really asking myself.

John Doe 128
New Orleans, LA 1995

I'm thinking about that wild boy I used to know. You
know, the young one with crazy black Hispanic eyes.

Motherfucker. You. I'd seen you around and caught your crazy eye. We flirted on the street. I knew you wanted it. So I went to the fag bar strip show contest. Your Spanish eyes widened when I caught you hustling on stage. You followed me all the way home like you were in a spell. It must have been 7 a.m. when we finally fell on my bed. Oh boy what a huge freak of a cock you have. Jesus Sweet Jesus. I am damned now. When we finished you accused me of being a witch like your mother and left hastily. Man, it took a year to get over you, your cock, you, your crazy Spanish eyes, your jokes, your laugh, your vulnerability, your bravado, your refusal.

I see you on Decatur Street in the bars now, a few years later. We don't speak, we avoid each other's eyes. Your face is bloated and older. You've lost your gaunt, hustler physique. And I can't help thinking how much thicker and fatter your freak cock must be.

John Doe 193
New York, NY 1999

'Hemingway never smoked cigarettes,' you slurred lighting our Winstons.

'Yeah, he thought it killed your sense of smell and you need that for the big hunt' I smiled and blew smoke in your face. That may be true about Hemingway but by your hand sliding up my leg, I'm certain you can smell my pussy in this smoke-filled bar.

BLACKOUT

Tyondai Braxton, Stefano Giovannini,
Thurston Moore, Lee Ranaldo, Leah Singer,
Matthew Wascovich

Originally Published: 2003

Introduction

In August, 2003, parts of the U.S. and Canada experienced the biggest electrical blackout in history covering some 9,300 square miles. What follows are poems and recollections tied to this event.

Light Pitch Black
Tyondai Braxton

Light pitch black, I'm gonna start shining bright, I'm gonna pitch light at the white shine, hold it in an arch and shine till I'm blind, bright white till the light shines black, you're gonna hold bright black light till it blinds the shine pitch white, I'm blind, shining bright light in an arch, bright black, pitch bright light at the arch till it starts blinding white pitch blind, Shining black light's gonna hold bright till blind light starts pitching white shine blind, arched till it holds light, shining till it blinds black, blind light's gonna blacken bright black till no light shines right, I'm white shining black in an arch, I'm black shining white in an arch, no blinds shine in light, right shine arches white in black, pitching bright shine till light holds blind light, till right holds no blinds, start right in a blind arch, hold shine till no light blinds bright, shine white, shine blind, shine black, start holding arched blind white, till all light blinds no bright light right, till no blind pitches start whitening light at no shine, all white light starts to arch till it's pitch black, all black light shines bright till bright lights blinds it pitch white, blackening arches till blind bright shines no white, white black light blinds all arches, blinds all pitches, brightens all shines, shines all light till it pitches held light at shining bright blind arches, all black light in all bright arches light white shines in blind brightness, black whiteness, blind shining rightness, till no arch holds all blinds, you're arches gonna shine it till no arches shine, till it blackens all black light in white pitches and held blind, Light

Pitch Black, you're right, I'm shining bright white in no white light AND pitch right at arched light arches AND shine bright black in a light blind white AND arch blind bright arches till it blinds AND black AND white shine right AND shine white AND shine blind AND shine black, start holding arched blind white till I'm holding you in blind light AND shine shine shine in a blind light blind, in a light arched black white till we're so blind, we're so white, we're so pitch black all light blinds arches till the black blind is at it's brightest light AND blind AND shine AND brighten all brightest blackest blind arches all pitched, hold it in an arch and shine we're blind

Untitled
Stefano Giovannini

on the night of the blackout i went to my ex- off
   and on ex-
i used to live wit—

so the black out was the black out of love—
makin' sure she was ok—she has some health problems—

and try to live a night far away from any external
   issue -
back to the bone of life -
now

i am in philly rite now—
some lover thing—
but i ain't happy—
got an email from my ex—
still kinda hurts to read her name
it is hard to be alone—
just slept with someone—but i don't feel things
    clicked—
they never click —

the fine faded boundary between escapism
and being trapped in the wrong situation.

i need communication —
healthy situations —
sex with laughter and lightness and communication.

i get hurt—
but people can't really hurt me anymore—
it is just the time—
and time takes away your dreams—and takes love
    away from you.
i live month by month—or night by night.
took some cool pictures—

but fuck it.
i feel a bit overwhelmed by stuff—
GC / $$$ / singleness / rejection / loss—
that sometimes i can be happy
sometimes i really wake up worried
about wasting my
life.

i wanna do a book- make more money—but i am
    low energy—
sex here in philly does not really cheer me up.

why did i not run away from frances in the begin-
    ning—
why did i stick with her? i ran away from women
    in the past—
women had ran away from me—
why did she stick with me and me with her?

was it just loneliness and desperation?

i am in a hurry

what worries me is not the blackout of electric
    power
but the blackout of emotional will

Untitled
Thurston Moore

black hair patty waters 1966 patti smith 1974 black
    eye james chance 1978
black man schooly d 1985 black woman jeanne lee
    1972 peace to be black free
to be black
out

Power to the people
Leah Singer

A hot day with air conditioners working over time it
is not unusual to think a power outage could happen.
It happened on a small scale last summer in fact.

Lee and band flew out that morning to Detroit to
play a big homecoming show for Iggy Pop and the
Stooges.

When the lights went out here and people started
flooding the streets and sidewalks outside my window
I decided to call Lee and tell him what was happening. As we spoke the lights went out in Detroit.

Living close to the World Trade Center site and still
having the 9/11 jitters I thought the worst. Lee was
able to get online and find out that the outage was
widespread. The first radio reports reassured everyone
that it was not an act of terrorism.

From there on I experienced the whole thing from

the viewpoint of my children. A small adventure was about to begin-my son delivered candles to the newsstand operators outside our building with my neighbor, we ate by candlelight, read by flashlight and slept in the same bed hugging plush animals. The next day was an ordinary day in the park. The cheap job lot stores did a brisk business in battery sales. We ate a lot of peanut butter. When the lights came back on after 23 hours we all screamed.

Iggy's gig was cancelled. We threw out the smelly yogurt and went looking for fresh milk.

Blacked Out August 2003
Lee Ranaldo

Sonic Youth fly early Thursday to Detroit/sonic youth to open for Iggy & the Stooges. The news reports on my way out the door promise it to be one of the very hottest days yet this summer. We pull up to amphitheatre/they are doing soundcheck—Mike Watt is singing as Iggy doesn't show for s.c. Shortly after they finish we're sitting with watt in our dressing room and he is regaling us with stories-we're talking Macintosh operating systems then American history then linguistics and always punkrock. Power flickers n goes out but we sit there and keep talking. It's out for awhile, 20 or 30 minutes. No big deal. My cel rings-it's Leah. Power is out in NYC. Funny, I tell her, it is here too. She says everyone is out on the street in

New York and wondering what the fuck is happening——things are 'back to normal' but everyone's still a little jumpy at anything out of the ordinary. Ready to be jumping. Wow this is weird the power is out there and here? Stories begin to filter in. Leah is concerned. Then celphone lines are jammed/what is happening?? Guys on the crew gather listening around car radios, doors and windows open in the summer sun——reports come in. 'power down from new york to detroit, up into Ontario too. Radio announcers voices filter into the heated air. No-one on air willing to utter the word 'terrorist' although it is everyones first question. Thurston tries to tune in the news on his little cassette recorder. All crackly and weak then static. We spend hours at the venue as the afternoon fades, all the seats empty, parking lot empty, people walking around not sure what to do. The show is canceled at 6 pm. Some friends who've driven and flown here to see this show hang out/make small talk. SY have another show in Chicago tomorrow. We are going to drive there in the large van we had rented for the day. At the hotel in Detroit they are handing out free ice cream bars as all the freezers are off and everything's melting. This goes on all across the blackout region. The grid is down. The power grid is down. It happened up by Niagara. It happened in New York City substation on 14th street. It happened out in ohio. Explosion. Fire. Nobody really knows. The grid is down. We're off the grid now. Candlelit. There's power 3 hours west of us. We have to drive back onto the grid. For hours we drive and the landscape is eerie, no lights on, people creeping across intersections without the benefit of traffic lights. Everyone is on best behavior which is odd for America. No reports of looting or anything like that. Post-9/11 there is a different consciousness about. Maybe that event will prove a singular catalyst in altering the way we city dwellers interact? Affect social change? We drive back onto the grid. We listen to the radio for news and watch DVDs on laptops in the van. It's dark out. They say Mars is at it's closest vantage point to the earth in 60,000 years but we fail to find it in the dark skies. A few days later our friend Stefano will email pictures of the darkened NY skyline from the Brooklyn bridge. Eerie. Leah says the children have fun eating dinner by candlelight/sleeping in one big bed in the dark. Chris said he went to Times Square just to lie down in the street and stare up at the dark skies—-amongst the businessmen and stranded tourists who were sleeping out that night—either because they were far from home or because the modern hotel rooms (w no windows that open!) were stifling hot. To lie down on 42nd Street and actually see the stars, not a haze of city-lights. He saw the stars from the center of the city of light. The stars are out. The lights are off. We drive back onto the grid. Slowly the northeast grid powers up again. The next night in Chicago I find Mars high and red in the southeastern skies.

unplug
Matthew Wascovich

tonight is an unstooge
like a dumb detroit on clampdown
call out the search lights
john's talking about chickens
larissa's in from florida
blasting five-year hugs
as the electric grid pops
and fizzles in new york
toronto cleveland
big north america blown
pass the bottled water
radical adults
burn candle dressing room style
valerie is a ghetto kid
on 7 mile road
bombed out michigan
depravity before ann arbor subdivide
lick the sweat and like it
blackout pieces
cops in the dark
throw food rot in the can
fukk it
the money is lost
it's trash
tomorrow in chicago
next to playboys
and cig fronts
death vibe goose fest

JIM GIRAFFE'S STORIES

Daren King

Originally Published: 2003

Jim has written some stories. He writes well, for a heathen. You can read some of his better efforts below:

FIRST STORY

This is the first story Jim ever wrote, when I'd just bought him the hoofwriter. He was having trouble working it.

asaasd
sadffffffffffffffffffffffffffffff
scsdcvvvvvvvvvvvvvvvvvvvvvvvvvvfssh
beeeeeeeeeeeeeeeeeeeeeeedr beer

A DAY AT THE ZOO

This next one is Jim's favourite. I'm not so keen. In

my opinion, it lacks warmth.

One day Jim and Daren went to the zoo. They saw some animals. The animals were in cages. Jim had a milkshake. Then, some dancing girls came along and gave Jim a kiss. Then, Daren started crying. I don't like him. He is rubbish.

THE PUB

There is a lot to be said for freedom of expression. However, there is a fine line between being creative and being an ignoramus, and this story crosses it. Jim, I am not happy.

Jim and Daren King and Alistair Canister went to the pub. Daren and Alistair didn't have any money so Jim bought the drinks. Jim had a pint of beer and Daren had shandy. Alistair wanted oil but they didn't have any so he had water. Then, Opinion Onion came in.

Jim said, 'What do you want to drink?' and he said he wanted a dry white wine. He wanted crisps so Jim bought him cheese & onion and he got cross.

Then, Jim bought drinks for everyone in the whole pub. Everyone likes him. He is really nice.

Then, some dancing girls came in. Jim bought them a bottle of champagne and they said they liked him and gave him their phone number.

Then Daren got killed.

GHOST TOWN

Tony O'Neill

Originally Published: 2004

6 months later spun out on crack, heroin and crystal meth once more, stinking and weak, homeless and friendless I tried to quit again. I was too scared to return to the apartment I had been renting on Black-burn Avenue because of a crazy stunt I had pulled the night before. I had let a dealer called Shakespeare crash there with a girl he was screwing in exchange for a couple of rocks of crack. When my crack was done though, I sneaked into the living room where he was passed out and I took the rest of his stash which I guessed correctly was in his shoe. I took that back to my room and smoked it compulsively, growing ever more paranoid that he would wake up and discover what I had done. To make matters worse, I knew that his uncle was involved in a gang called 'El M' and that this act of stupidity would not go unpunished. I stuffed my clothes into a holdall and abandoned

the apartment at 6 in the morning, cracked out and insane with fear while they slept on.

I hadn't paid rent in 2 months and realized that eviction proceedings must surely be under way by now anyway. I needed a place to stay and a chance to get through the worst of my cold turkey.

The guesthouse I ended up crashing in was located at the back of a friend's house, in an area of Venice known locally as ghost town. It was a slum area with a thriving crack scene and what seemed like no apparent sources for heroin whatsoever. The couple who had let me take over their guest room for a few weeks were quite well off, worthy and well intentioned although I was rapidly getting sick of their concerns about my health. Broke and scared I had called them up telling them that I was trying to come off of heroin again but couldn't do it in Hollywood. They offered me the guesthouse as a place to stay while I got through the worst of the physical symptoms and I accepted gratefully. Three days after arriving there I realized that – yet again – I did not have the strength or endurance to get through the next weeks cold turkey. I needed to get heroin somehow, so that night I hit the street trying to score.

For a junky, the place really was a ghost town. At first I got excited when I walked around – on virtually every street corner guys loitered whistling at cars as they cruised past, running up to the vehicles which pulled up and making sales. In dark corners, pressed against walls like statues, ebony figures appraised the foot traffic in the area. Some kids used laser pointers in what seemed to be a code to warn of approaching cops, shabbily dressed buyers tried to hawk boom boxes, jewellery and other shit in exchange for drugs. I stepped over an older white guy who had obviously just been jacked for money, drugs or both. He was lying face down on the street, the back of his head smashed open and raw. It was a street-dealing scene almost as busy as Macarthur Park. However, after hitting the first three guys I came up to and getting offered nothing more than crack or PCP I started to get a sinking feeling. I only had 40 dollars on me, and in my sick state my overriding need was for heroin, not substitute drugs.

I finally found an old looking crack head skulking around the darker recesses of a basketball court on Rose. He watched me approach with a smirk. There weren't too many white kids walking around this area so late at night. He had me pegged for a junky straight away.

'Hey' I said as I walked towards him.

'Hey yourself,' he replied with a voice so deep it was almost subliminal, 'You looking for someone?'

'Look, I need to score man. I'm looking for chiva. Dope—you know where I can get some?'

'Chiva?' the old guy whistled, 'You in the wrong place. All rocks around here son. I can do you a good deal on some rocks…'

'Listen I'm a junky and I'm sick. All I'm looking for

is dope.'

'Well…' the old guy said thoughtfully, 'You're gonna be a looking motherfucker then 'cos ain't no market for that round here. People want rocks they come here. People want that shit they go downtown.'

I thanked him and walked back to the guesthouse. It was eleven at night and I had no car. I was screwed. I went back to bed, took 5 10 milligram Valiums and tried to sleep. The night seemed endless. As the sleeping pills took hold I managed to fall into a drugged half sleep for a couple of hours, but by 2:30 in the morning I was wide awake again, wet with junk sweat, and doubled over with stomach cramps. I watched the sun rise on the wall of my room, checking the clock every ten minutes convinced an hour must have passed by now. I vomited continuously into the trashcan by my bed, even when my stomach was empty still having to lean over and regurgitate burning yellow stomach acid every so often.

I called Raphael as soon as 8 the next morning crawled by. He seemed surprised to hear from me, and even more surprised when I told him where I was staying. He told me that he'd figured I'd gotten busted or OD'd so I filled him in a little on what had been happening. I asked him for a 20-dollar bag of smack and he reluctantly agreed to drive it out to me. He always bitched when I wanted less than half a gram delivered, but I was insistent. I gave him detailed directions and he told me he'd be here at 9:30. I agreed to meet him a few blocks away and I settled down to wait.

This was the beginning of my third day without dope. Stomach cramps were increasing in their ferocity and all of my demons where coming to the surface, lurking under the bed and in the closet... Again I became totally aware of my situation, of the utter hopelessness of where I was and what I was about to do. I get 20 dollars worth of smack and then what? When it runs out I am back to where I started... less money, starting my kick all over again. A black chasm of despair opened up inside of me. A month in detox and rehab and here I was 4 months later strung out worse than ever, out of money sleeping in the guesthouse of some people I barely know. None of my friends from before I got a habit wanted to know me. So much time had passed since my last success with a band that I had faded totally from the collective consciousness, everyone who worked for our band at the label had moved on, no one remembered. And here I was, stuck in this shit-hole area of Venice, dope sick and miserable about to extend my misery for one more afternoon of tranquillity. Stuck on the other side of the world from my old friends, my old life. I was miserable. I wanted this to stop; I really wanted it to stop. I didn't just want a break from the drugs; I wanted to go back to before I stuck a needle in my arm for the first time, before I knew how fucking amazing that feeling is, before I blew it for myself by getting a taste of what heaven must feel like. How could I go back to blissful ignorance now? Despite the dire situation I was now in and how unhappy it made me, I knew that the sad truth was that being straight, getting out of bed and starting the day without a shot of dope just wasn't a possible reality for me any more. How could I live with the horrors and the boredom of being alive without something to make me feel that it was worthwhile, something to make me feel connected to the world around me? I'd changed. I'd altered my brain chemistry, my reward system my entire outlook on life and as far as I could see the change was irreversible. I had no more control over what happened next than I had over the wind or the rain. I was at my habits mercy.

It was late morning when my phone finally went off. I had lain there, squirming and cursing, puking and spitting, staring and the impertinent mute thing, willing it to buzz into life to no avail. I had actually started to sleep when the phone did go off, and I snatched it up before the first ring had ended. Raphael's voice was the most beautiful thing I had ever heard at that moment and I gasped 'On my way' before hanging up. I got up wearing only jeans and a T-shirt, no shoes no socks. I had a sense of purpose now, like a long distance runner beginning his journey. I was focused totally on the transaction, on getting to Raphael as soon as possible, and then getting back so I could obliterate my feelings for another few hours. All those hours in rehab, sat cross legged in a circle, concentrating on breathing and trying – unsuccessfully -to achieve the kind of spiritual peace though meditation that I am suddenly bestowed with while going to score. Maybe this is the closest I am ever going to get to that kind of bliss – my situation is suddenly cropped and reduced down to the bare essentials for now – I will leave, I will score, I will get high. Beyond that the world is an irrelevancy.

I left the house, nervously fingering the scrunched up 20 in my pocket. As soon as I had walked a couple of steps down the block the heat rising from the pavement started to burn the soles of my feet. Well, fuck it. I considered the delay that returning to the guest house for a pair of shoes would entail and deciding against it I turned left on Rose and carried on walking the 7 or 8 blocks to where I was due to meet Raphael. The sidewalk changed from broken paving slabs to tarmac and the tarmac was beginning to melt already under the desert sun. I could feel its softness under my feet and became aware that it was beginning to stick to them. Each step became more and more painful. I could feel blisters forming, and I started to try and walk on the sides of my feet to take some of the pressure off my burning soles. The sun beat down mercilessly, but I fixed my mind on the drugs I was going to buy and like some old Indian yogi walking on hot coals, the thought of fixing put the thoughts of my breaking and blistering flesh to the back of my mind.

I made it to a strip mall on the corner of Rose and Lincoln consisting of a Chinese take away, cheque cashing place, pawn shop and a Laundromat. I ducked into a shaded spot and sat on the wall waiting for Raphael to show. I watched every passing car intently looking for his face behind the wheel of his junkyard Toyota. A new looking SUV pulled into the lot and I was surprised to see Raphael behind the wheel with a new girlfriend. I wondered absently if he'd finally stopped drinking and snorting and whoring every dollar he made. I limped over and slid into the cool, air-conditioned vehicle. I closed my eyes, enjoying the feel of the leather seats and the cool air. I couldn't help but notice our change of circumstances. When I first met Raphael he was working the corner of Pico and Coronado in ripped sneakers, hustling for a dollar. I had a car, an apartment and a life. And now here I was, broke and broken, climbing into his new, air-conditioned ride.

'Hey buddy' Raphael grinned, turning round to face me, 'You don't look so good.'

His girlfriend turned to look at me and turned away just as quickly with a slightly disgusted look on her face. She muttered something in Spanish and started fixing her lipstick.

'I don't feel so good my friend'

We did the deal and Raphael dropped me on the corner of my street. I thanked him, told him I'd be in touch and split with my drugs. There's not a lot of small talk to be done between a dealer and a customer once the transaction is completed. If only all human interactions were so clean cut and defined. I carefully slid the front gate open, and walked back into the house. Standing in the yard and watering the plants was Jim, one of the people who took me in this time. He looked up at me and raised an eyebrow.

'Hey… What you doing up? I thought you'd be… well, you know.'

Jim was in his fifties and had been on the periphery of the music industry for most of his life. He made his living training corporations how to make more money by employing some kind of new age psychobabble that he tried to explain to me once, but my overriding impression of him was the bitterness that he carried around at never making it as a musician. Maybe this is why he still tolerated me coming around to borrow money that I could never pay back, asking for a place to stay when things were bad. He probably thought of me as a colourful character and I was sure I made a funny topic of conversation when he hung out with his friends, that I was some kind of attempt to hang on to his past in the rock industry. It made me feel like even more of a whore and a loser. Instead of sucking his cock I was here to be a performing monkey, to fit into some stereotype of an artist on the ropes. An artist who hadn't done anything more than shoot up for the past two years. Jim smoked pot and claimed to understand my problems, yet he thought it was as easy as just putting the needle down for me to get straight. Right now I was not in the mood for his homilies.

'Yeah I'm not feeling so good. Tried to take a walk to clear my head but I didn't get far' I gestured to my bare feet, 'To hot to go more than a block without shoes in this weather.'

'I'll say!' he laughed with mock concern, 'You look pretty bad. You are doing the right thing though. That shit will kill you, know what I'm saying?'

I stared right through him, focusing on getting past him, into the guesthouse and fixing.

'You're right Jim. I'm over it. I just need to get my strength back and I'll be cool.'

'Good man' he gave me a friendly tap on the shoulder and I tried not to recoil from it, 'keep it up'

I walked past him thinking 'FUCK YOU JIM, FUCK YOU FUCK YOU' but saying something about going for a lie down as I slipped inside my room to get myself well again. I split the 20 bag in two and shot into my neck for the sake of speed. I was shaky and weak and the idea of finding a vein anywhere else in a hurry seemed pretty remote. The shot instantly flooded my system with good feelings. I didn't get very high, but a familiar warmth radiated within me. A feeling of coming home.

I spent the day in a pleasant state of blessed out lethargy. Suddenly I had an interest in TV, music, writing again. I scribbled in my journal a little, ate some cakes and chocolates from the fridge, dozed off for a while. I awoke some time later, when the sun had set and something dark had rose in my heart. I looked at my pathetic wrap of smack and resisted the urge to do it. I wasn't sick yet. Again the thought of what would happen when I ran out surfaced and I felt a pang of psychosomatic withdrawal symptoms simply from thinking about it. I stood up with a new sense of purpose. I started hunting around for the last of my money, as always figuring the best way to not think about my situation. I was going to get high, and if there was no heroin in Ghost Town then I suppose I'd have to smoke crack. I rustled up 40 dollars in bills and change and headed out of the back door.

An hour later and I was sat with Henry and Arturo, two members of a street gang called the V13 (V for Venice, 13 for the thirteenth letter of the alphabet which is M for Mexico). I was cooking up a rock of crack in lemon juice sourced straight from the lemon tree growing out the back of the guest house and they watched me with mounting horror as I cooked it up, filtered it into a syringe and started digging for a vein.

'Man, shooting crack' Henry grumbled, shaking his head and looking at the floor 'that's some prison shit right there.'

Henry was a man mountain; a local crack dealer covered in jailhouse and gang tattoos and so it seemed absurdly comical that the sight of my cooking up and injecting crack shocked him. I smirked for a second, before returning to the job in hand and focusing my attention to finding a suitable vein. As I pushed the concoction into a vein it stung – lemon juice is caustic especially when administered intravenously. The hit was good, that familiar rush of adrenaline that comes from shooting coke took me and after glazing over for a moment I came back to situation at hand.

Earlier on I had scored a rock off of Henry and took it back to the guesthouse. I didn't have a pipe, so I picked a lemon from out the back and injected the rock. I licked it first and as it tasted like coke, not soap or wax I felt somewhat reassured about shooting it. The rush was good, so I headed out with the rest of my money to buy some more.

Henry talked a little more this time. He asked me if I was new to the area, if I lived nearby. I told him that I was 2 blocks away and he made me an offer. If he and his homeboy Arturo could come back to my place and have a smoke they would provide the pipe and a few free rocks. I was pretty looped on crack so I decided that this was a fine idea and Henry gave a coded whistle summoning Arturo – a dealer ensconced on a further street corner over. Introductions where made and we all headed back to the guesthouse. As Henry and Arturo made a bong out of a glass stem, some gauze and a soda bottle I prepared a fix...

The pipe went round a few times, with the usually intensity of a crack sessions with strangers. Conversation was stilted and forced, and tended to drift off as we watched each other load the pipe and take a hit with starving eyes. Things only relaxed when the pipe was in my hand and I could concentrate on putting a rock on the gauze, holding a light to the stem, filling my lungs with the smoke, bellowing out plumes of white cocaine fumes, feeling the rush dizzying me and almost as quickly starting to fade as I passed the pipe on and resumed watching intently and awaiting another turn...

Pretty soon the crack was gone and Arturo turned to me.

'Lets go for a drive' he said, 'We gotta pick up some more.'

Cruising the back streets of Ghost Town, Henry at the wheel with Arturo lighting a joint laced with angel dust and me in the back seat, I started to get a bad feeling. My adrenaline was pumped up to insane levels and my guts churning in anticipation of something indefinable yet terrifying. Henry was circling a block with a set of projects on it shadowed with palm trees and whispering conspiratorially with Arturo. The joint was passed back to me but I refused it as the very smell of PCP was making me feel sick. I kept my eyes firmly on the guys in the front seat and my hand on the door handle in case I needed to bail out.

There was a kid hanging out on the corner and upon noticing him Henry whispered, 'here we go' killing the lights and turning into a side street half a block up from the kid. I watched as Arturo pulled a gun and a balaclava out of the glove box, and slid the balaclava over his head, sticking the piece in his jacket pocket. I kept quiet. Silently he opened the car door, and slipped off into the night.

'What the fuck is he going to do?' I hissed to Henry after Arturo is gone.

'A debt. That nigger workin' the corner is getting jacked, man. Fucking pussy.'

The silence of the night hung all around us in the balmy air. I heard the crackle of the pot burning as Henry took a drag. The chemical smell from the angel dust filled the car. I kept an eye on the street around us but it seemed completely deserted.

Suddenly Arturo turned the corner, still wearing his balaclava and slumped into the passenger seat. Henry gunned the engine and we took off back towards the guesthouse. I watched Arturo place the gun back in the glove box, and even in the dark I could see it was slick with blood.

'Here cop this' Arturo told me, as he shoved something back towards my hand. I opened my palm and he dumped a bloody mess into it. In the red goop were 7 or 8 cellophane wrapped rocks and one smashed front tooth. I brushed the tooth to the floor with a shudder and closed my fist around the drugs.

'Watch the blood there,' Arturo told me dryly, 'I had to knock the shit out of the jungle-bunny's mouth.'

DANGER STRANGER

Richard Cabut

Originally Published: 2004

'Danger stranger,' sings Carol in the bathroom while putting on her make-up. 'You better paint your face.'

Yeah, she thinks: better paint your face so people don't notice the spots, scabs, scars, bruises, pock marks, bite sites, and common or garden pustule craters. Each blemish a memory, marking her skin to make up a map of mad experience. Signs pointing to excess, ineptitude, waste, squander and self-disgust.

The lyrics are from the old Clash song "1977" describing, amongst other things, the poor, class warfare and meltdown on the streets—sten guns in Knightsbridge. At that time, Carol called herself by names like Rancid, Piss and Suck to create a cheeky distance from the nauseating niceness of society. Now, after 27 odd—very odd—years of hard living (some of which have involved coming perilously close to dying) such monikers are but casual insults hurled at her in the streets and pubs of New Cross and Peckham, south London, the area she calls home—'Where the heartache is', she says to herself.

Carol pats her growing gut. Up the stick again? No, but the atmosphere of this place is impregnated with a sense of failure and fucked-upness, she thinks.

Earlier, on Commercial Street, Carol had seen a black cat unlucky enough to have been hit by a car—or given a vicious kicking by some particularly stupid and sadistic kids. With cracked back and smashed head, the broken little beast flipped around like a landed fish in the middle of the road. Eyes rolled and blood sprayed from a shattered mouth, as the cat danced its violent death flip. Carol shuddered and moved on. Her universe, full of portents and signs, was marked by a sense of melancholy, isolation and the stomach-churning premonition that it is all going to go tits up. This is a bad sign, she thought.

Carol lives in a Peckham maisonette with two small children and a succession of different lovers—although what love's got to do with it is anyone's guess, she thinks. Here, there is no Only Fools and Horses-style jollity, but plenty of fucking fools, though, thinks Carol, especially the ones who buy the near gear from a dodgy dealer down the road. Or, those who queue for the rubbish bootleg DVDs from the Chinese man at the bottom of Rye Lane, situated a hop, skip and a stumble from the boozer Carol sometimes uses in Nunhead. There are nearer pubs—but hey, she thinks—those are for doomed losers.

Later, down the boozer, Carol is really pissed, hasn't been so off her head for a long time. In fact, the last time it happened on such a scale, she had woken up with a strange bloke. Nothing unusual about that, but this one had a really big black eye, at which Carol had burst out laughing. The bloke looked at her.

'I wouldn't laugh so loud if I was you, darling,' he said. 'Take a look in the mirror.'

Aggh! Carol couldn't believe her eyes. Where her two front teeth should be was a neat gap. Somehow, between leaving the pub and falling asleep, her teeth had been knocked out. How? Carol had no idea. The grandparents of Carol's first child were due round any time to take the kid out for the day—which was more than the father ever did. If there was any shit, any suggestion of bother, they'd try to take the kid away from her, that's for sure. Carol, head in hands, groaned.

Now in the pub, Carol is steaming after another bad day, when her youngest had been sent home from the nursery for hitting another kid. 'He gets violent an' they can't handle him,' she told a mate. 'But all they gotta do is put their arms around him, hold him for a bit and he's all right. But they don't bother.' The nursery incident had put the kibosh on a work shift, helping the bloke who sells the international phone cards. Instead, she spent her time feeding videos into the machine and crisps into the kid in the hope of getting some free head space. But after a couple of hours, Carol knew the only way to get through the day without going stark staring was to pop to the offy for a few cans. Whatever it takes to get through the day, she thought. It was no big drama involving changes in the order of the universe, just everyday wear and tear while standing in the debris of ennui and hope denied. The kid is safely in the hands of a mate, who said to the pub-bound Carol: 'Be careful out there,' in an American accent, like that yank TV cop.

In the Duke of Connaught, Carol is the nub of the hubbub. Tottering precariously from one drinker to another, the more drunk she gets the more of a hunk he becomes—if you put on dark glasses, squint, avoid noticing the beer gut and turn away when he speaks in order to dodge the dog breath. Flirting, flashing a bit of tit (no nipples, though—she has her principles) and shouting out stuff during the pub quiz, like: 'Who's the drummer in Oasis? Dunno, but I bet he's got a tiny cock. And I bet he can't get it up in any case—like most of the alkies in 'ere!'

Her conversation is loaded with trash innuendo and outrage: harmless nonsense; rubbish one-liners; the blessing of talking bollocks. Some, though, are annoyed by Carol's cocky craziness. They think of her as … provocative, and Carol gets some funny looks from some very unfunny geezers; monsters seemingly disgorged by some dark underground.

Be careful out there.

'The best thing about being a bloke,' says Mark to

some other blokes while wiping lager spillage from his face. 'Is that even going to the toilet is a bonus.'

Eyebrows are raised in puzzlement.

'When I have a slash,' he continues, 'and I've finished, yeah?'

Yeah?

'Well, I squeeze instead of shake.'

Yeah?

'Some blokes shake the last drops of piss out, but I squeeze—four or five times, that's all; enough to get a bit of feeling down there.'

'Don't get me wrong,' he continues, arms spread. 'I don't overdo it—I don't wanna be waltzing about the kharzi with a hard on, some fuckers might get the wrong idea.'

'Just enough to put a smile on my face—or, rather, on me head,' he adds, frowning because he's not sure whether he should have talked so openly about his toilet habits.

'Ah, fuck it,' he says. 'I'm going for a piss.'

The others jeer his back, making wanker signs. He turns around looking daggers—a stare caught by Carol, who thinks: what a tosser.

Be careful.

But there are others in the pub who would certainly not dare to talk out loud about their extracurricular activities, their little peccadillos. Peter, for instance, who has the anti-social habit of, while in other people's bathrooms, wiping his dirty penis on their towels. Later, he fantasises about how his most private of parts has no doubt touched the faces—lips! —of women, his mates' wives and daughters who have, in turn, used those towels. Peter looks at Carol as she passes.

'I hate ugly birds,' he says.

'They're all right,' says Don.

'How do you make that out?'

'If they're ugly, you can do what you want to them in bed. Do disgusting things you wouldn't dare do to an ordinary person. Be really horrible. And they take it, cos they know they're ugly, and they're lucky to get anything at all. Even if it's a slap and a kick, they're grateful. And then you boot them out in the morning.'

'Reminds me of the 60s,' says Peter, who spent the Summer of Love spreading diseases.

Out there.

Carol vaguely hears this conversation, and absorbs it through the fuzz of booze. Her energy has dissipated to the extent that she thinks about getting home, navigating the endless possibilities of brutalist council estates, sweltering in the summer night. The place is floundering, dehydrated, dying from lack. Speed frozen.

Be careful.

'So this machine…' pontificates a bloke, whose face suddenly contorts in anger after noticing his newly-poured pint of bitter.

'Oi, darling, I said lager,' he screams at the barmaid.

'I thought you wanted…' she starts.

'Nah,' he says.

'I thought…' she half whispers.

'Listen darling,' he says, making sure he's got the attention of the blokes at the bar. 'Don't think. What you want to do is take another tablet, luv. Take another pill to help you with your head cos this pill, the one you've obviously been taking, isn't doing anything for you. Cos you're still stupid. You need something to make you a bit cleverer, girl. You need a clever pill. Just do us a favour and don't think.'

Everyone laughs as the red-faced barmaid pours another pint. Of lager.

'…sell the machine for £400…' continues the bloke, who is interrupted by the barmaid trying to make amends by joining in with the mob.

'Why?' she enquires about the machine.

The man looks at her, then at his friends, and then at the barmaid again.

'Do you want me to draw you a diagram, luv!? he says.

'But…'

'Paint you a picture, darling?'

'But…'

'Do a little Pic-arse-hole, so that you can see what I'm on about?' he shouts: 'IT'S NOT FUCKING ROCKET SCIENCE.'

Carol makes it to the toilet cubicle, drool coming out of her mouth, but avoids being sick. 'Fuck,' she says. 'Fuck fuck fuck,' and wishes she hadn't given her number to a couple of the pub psychos before she realised they were animals, wishes she hadn't told the mental geezer with the toupee that he could walk home with her, wishes she hadn't said at the bar, 'I don't care if people think I'm a slag just cos I like blokes. I don't care.'

Some people, she now thinks, may have taken it the wrong way. Carol smells of gin and lager and lime and regret.

The graffiti on the cubicle door reads: 'Stuck? Have a wank!'

Yeah, right, Carol thinks. Instead, she pulls out her mobile.

A few people look on expectantly as Carol walks out of the bog. For instance the bloke, bulging with hang-ups and depravities, who all evening has been puzzling about the length of Carol's toenails, the state of her underpants—slightly soiled or really rank? he wonders—and the amount of undigested food in her stomach. 'She looks like she's just farted,' he says. And that other chap who, if he could be bothered, would feel really bad about the porn he watches: anything involving skewers, needles, or electricity.

As Carol moves away from them in the direction of the door, a few men stand up to follow. A faraway energy envelopes everything: fear.

Outside, a trashed old couch, springs uncoiling, nestles in the corner of some waste ground. A small black cat slinks through the humid evening. There is the squeal of tyre rubber on tarmac.

Carol stops. So do the men.

Another bloke looks up from his paper and says to his mate. 'Why are tales of poor people, the underclass, those who encounter daily aggro, crime, humiliation, disappointment and death, so titillating to literary thrill-seekers looking for books in which the dirt is a credential of reality?'

There is no answer.

Carol gulps. The men smile.

Suddenly, the door opens. A bloke walks in.

'Mini cab for Carol?' he asks.

Carol breathes an audible sigh of relief. The sense of disappointment emanating from the men is almost palpable and compensatory rounds are ordered.

The cab driver looks around the boozer, takes in the vicious vibe, and leads Carol by the arm. 'Come on,' he says, 'Let's go.'

A parting v-sign, and Carol stumbles out of the door. Once more, she has looked into the abyss, but managed to break off the hypnotic, calamitous gaze before being sucked in.

'It was getting a bit iffy in there,' she says to the cabby. 'Glad you responded to my call so quick.'

'Come on,' he pulls, his grip tightening on her arm.

'Where's your cab?' she asks.

'Don't worry,' he says. 'It's just round the corner,' he points to somewhere vague, dark and desolate.

There is silence for a minute while things sink in.

Be careful out there?

Too late.

'Front or back?' he asks, rhetorically, as they approach his car.

Front or back? You couldn't make it up, she thinks, dragged into the undertow of a dreadful dream with its unsettling logic, a silence in which a truth can be glancingly confronted—a truth which makes clear that in life, as in melodrama, those of ill-luck and no prospects are usually allowed to escape from sticky situations into even stickier ones.

'You couldn't make it up,' says Carol, to no one, really.

THE MORRISSEY EXHIBITION

HP Tinker

Originally Published: 2004

The Morrissey Exhibition is a beautiful place, crammed with wonder, the furniture of dreams. Spread over four exquisitely furnished floors, the exhibition houses the largest collection of privately-owned Morrissey arte-facts in the world... 35,000 or so Morrissey-related exhibits, including...

- Morrissey's priceless collection of identical Panama hats.
- A plinth containing Sonny Liston.
- Selected feedback (1992/1995)
- A recently restored childhood trowel.
- Gilbert O'Sullivan's monogrammed golf-ball, once used by Morrissey.

The Morrissey Exhibition should initially be visited when you are at a particularly low ebb, possibly having a hard time understanding your cat's death or why your mother is attached to a respirator. When you stroll around the Morrissey Exhibition such things make greater sense.

It is a time for contemplation as much as celebration.

Later, you will repeat the experience, several times, probably with a close companion.

On the steps of the Morrissey Exhibition you can ponder out loud:

'I wonder which way our lives are going?'

Nobody will answer, of course…

So try asking the same question again, with slightly adjusted phrasing.

'Who knows?' someone will reply, eventually. 'Life is unpredictable, basically. That's the thing. It doesn't tend to resemble most modern American fiction. It's hard to gauge, being both meaningful and meaningless at the same time, more or less.

(NOTE. On the steps of the Morrissey Exhibition, JB Priestley is immortalised thoughtfully in brass, stroking his chin. Has this any known connection to the Morrissey Exhibition? Nobody is sure. This is just one of the many enigmas associated with the Morrissey Exhibition.)

There are other attractions designed to compel your attention.

On Tuesdays, there's the rare video demonstration of Morrissey's telepathic powers. On the second floor, the Troy Tate Gallery houses thousands of exclusive personal polaroids: Morrissey at the Casino (1981), riding a bicycle (1964), contacting the dead (1988), wearing a rubber ring (1999), looking aggrieved at the site of the Peterloo Massacre, date unknown.

Meanwhile, in the listening room, the entire Morrissey back catalogue is continually played in reverse, an instructive experience you will find.

Celebrity guest have been known to make unexpected appearances too: Leo Sayer performing "November Spawned A Monster" on the harmonium... Germaine Greer dancing the Watusi in a tutu... David Bowie stranded on one knee, weakly grasping a tulip. (During the interval, he will bend cutlery and play the spoons, if asked politely.)

The public flagellation of Mark Simpson is also a highly popular event.

Scattered through the foyer, several ex-members of Herman's Hermits are strategically positioned, in aspic, although not technically available for general purchase. Official merchandise is for sale, however, much nearer the exit where you can purchase an authenticated limited edition wine sample from Ron Mael's semi-retired moustache should you so desire...

The foyer of the Morrissey Exhibition is repudiated to be heavy with paranormal activity. Some say the ghost of Mickey Finn has been sighted looking slightly dejected, worried about things in general... nobody actually knows why.

Dedicatedly non-elitist, the Morrissey Exhibition boasts an unusually urbane carpeting scheme throughout which can disorientate the inexperienced visitor. You can certainly get lost in there. Totally lost. Completely lost. Utterly lost. Horribly, horribly lost. So horribly lost that you fear you might never find yourself again. What level am I on? you may well ask, on occasion. Is that way up or down? What's through that door? Where in the name of Jesus am I? The experience of wandering through the Morrissey Exhibition is a constantly bewildering, exhilarating, ultimately rewarding process...

There's a short guided tour through Morrissey's subconscious (Saturdays only) and few remain unmoved by this experience. Teenagers of all sizes have been known to produce whole buckets of tears. All security staff carry emergency buckets in case of excessive weeping. The walls have been reinforced to withstand the depth of such emotion: 'I am normally not like this,' several people will tell you, cheerfully sobbing to themselves, wracked with rare, usually unfelt, poignant depths.

So, who finds love at the Morrissey Exhibition? The girl with the dancing breasts? The duelling Glaswegian? The lipstick librarian? The balding curator?

Nobody, it seems... nobody finds love within those walls... love steadfastly eludes all those who attend the Morrissey Exhibition.

However, you may be fondled repeatedly during your visit...

Moreover, you may be bitten ferociously on the

nape of the neck by handsome young strangers who will bedazzle you with tantalizing questions only to disguise themselves later with tall hats so you won't ever recognise them again.

Although love is frequently absent from within the perimeters of the Morrissey Exhibition, once I touched you there. Oh, yes. I did. Most definitely. At least, I thought I did. Or—at least—you touched me. It was one way or the other. Didn't you notice? Much later, under quite different circumstances, you seemed decidedly under impressed. So maybe I didn't touch you as much as I thought I had, maybe I didn't touch you at all. Maybe I only thought I'd touched you and I was mistaken. Maybe you wanted me to think I'd touched you and then regretted it the next morning. Maybe I did touch you, a little, but you got embarrassed by the whole thing and you decided to act like it had never happened. The exact train of events is not clear to me, never was. And the whole episode has left me visibly saddened...

Was that your aim, then? To sadden me visibly in public?

Beware. The balding curator of the Morrissey Exhibition sees everything. Watching over the proceedings, wryly, from a raised platform in the foyer, maintaining an impenetrable mask of enigma. (Is that a smile on his face? A tear in his eye? Who can truthfully tell? And what is his ultimate purpose? How does he spend his free time outside of the Morrissey Exhibition?)

'The Morrissey Exhibition is available for functions,' the balding curator tells people. 'In fact, there's a lesbian wedding in the basement at this very moment... they are dancing topless as we speak...'

Marvellous new exhibits about to be unveiled at the Morrissey Exhibition:

- His dream-stained teenage pillow.
- A packet of Fox's Glacier Mints (1991, unused).
- Johnny Tillotson's criminal record.
- A leather garter once modelled by Violet Carson.
- The small earthquake experienced personally by Morrissey himself on 3rd July 2002.

The balding curator is outwardly pleased with his new exhibits, inwardly pleased with himself. Silently, buried beneath a mask of discontentment, disenchantment, he marvels at the never-ending resourcefulness of his own nature... privately wondering if his life is travelling in the direction he originally planned, privately wondering if his life is travelling in any recognisable direction at all...

Morrissey himself, of course, is never in attendance. This is, mostly likely, due to the fact that he has several better things to do. Instead, over-weight bunny girls and waspish excitement can be found frequenting the exhibition excitedly on his behalf...

Sadly, there will come a time when you sit down on

a hard-backed chair and ask yourself: is this the right moment to leave the Morrissey Exhibition? How can I extricate myself safely and securely without causing further complication? My companion has aged considerably since our arrival. Time has unfairly ravaged her. Did we stay too long at the Morrissey Exhibition? Did we outlast our welcome? There are such sights within the Morrissey Exhibition, you see... but did they ever really exist anywhere other than in our collective ponderings? And if we do leave, will we ever go back? Perhaps not, but we feel all the more human for having spent just a few hours there...

And so, holding hands on the steps of the Morrissey Exhibition, under the economical gaze of JB Priestly, we part, like former lovers. We don't look back.

No. Not for one moment. No. Not at all. Why should we?

It is armed with nothing more than regret that I return to my other life.

THREE PUB REVIEWS

Paul Ewen

Originally Published: 2004

The Champion, Fitzrovia

The most pleasant barmaid in The Champion regarded me queerly, no doubt astounded that she could casually observe my arteries and intestinal workings in operation. Let me explain. I had been scuffing my shoes along the back roads of Fitzrovia, waving out to passing red postal trucks, when I'd decided to drop into that great corner pub that is The Champion. Inside I found much character, jovial patrons and a truly winning atmosphere.

The upstairs bar was packed with dining customers and extra seating, but it was the downstairs area that really made The Champion the institution it was and is. Large white and brown square tiles lined the floor around the bar, and seating was comprised of chocolate brown leather benches and many comfortable bar stools. There was a special little darts alley, and a brown tombstone shaped sign behind the bar read: 'Please Keep Clear for Glass Collection.' However, the real highlights of this great boozer, which made my eyes sparkle in myriads of kaleidoscopic spheres, were the beautiful stained glass windows featuring images of genuine British champions. David Livingstone the intrepid explorer was pictured carrying a rifle over his shoulder, a cane in hand, and his sideburns looked uncannily like the floor mats just inside the doors. William Renshaw was the winner of seven singles and seven doubles tennis cups. With his brother he made lawn tennis into a sport and apparently he was fond of wearing brown slippers.

I raised my glass to David, William, and to all the other great British champions preserved in glass around the bar, and I was surprised to find myself getting misty eyed at their accomplishments. But as I held aloft my cold beer, I was even more surprised to notice that my hand was actually misting up also. I wiped a clean circle of mist on my forearm, and I looked right through it to see my foot. I looked right through my foot and saw a brown tile. My entire body had turned to glass! I laughed out loud, but it wasn't my normal laugh. It sounded like the noise you make when you run a wet finger around the rim of a glass, and I guess it was the culmination of my saliva and glass larynx. My drinking vessel and the ashtray on my table suddenly seemed like brothers to me, and I gazed around the front of the bar at the established champions that welcomed me from their glass walls. There wasn't a spare window space ready for me, so I knew in the meantime I would have to tread very carefully in my clearly fragile body.

I walked with precise and calculated steps towards the bar, attracting the puzzled stares of others, who were no doubt drawn by the clinking sound of my feet resonating on the square tiled floor like a champagne flute being flicked. I was careful not to chip my toes on the golden tubular footrest that ran around the bottom of the serving area, and I sought out a clean bar towel and set about polishing myself until I gleamed like one of your gran's royal wedding souvenir goblets. My new falsetto voice sounded like a choirboy's as I ordered another drink, and the barmaid stared perhaps too long at my quivering heart that pumped blood around my delicate glass interior. After carefully making my way back to my seat, I made a start on my drink and amused myself for a while by watching it run down into my see-through stomach and slosh around. This was particularly funny when I twisted my hips a bit. I could have amused myself for hours with this of course, but looking around at the various glass champions that lined the windows, I felt an impatient longing to take my rightful place amongst them. So I stood on one of the dark chocolate leather bench seats and gently leaned against the cocoa wall, assuming a pose with raised drink in my right hand and chin rested atop the shiny knuckles of my left. You could say I was debonair and perhaps even rather dashing. 'I'm shy really,' I said with a bashful smile to the approaching barmaid, but my smile was somewhat lost on her, perhaps behind her apron, and she demanded that I get my filthy bowling shoes off the bar seating. I protested of course, resisting her outstretched hand, instead resuming a new pose that revolved around fingering a feathery quill.

Unfortunately, I kind of lost my balance at this point, falling sideways off the bench seat across a small round bar table with black wrought iron legs. The subsequent noise kind of sounded like a stolen truck being driven through a department store window, and I instantly smashed into one hundred thousand shards all across the white and brown square tiles. However, the quick thinking and attentive staff soon had me swept up into a plastic tray, and after pouring me into a newspaper and folding this into a rough ball, I was added to the cigarette butts and empty peanut packets in the large rubbish bin out back.

The Champion, Fitzrovia W1T 3PA

Prince George, Hackney

I was seated at the far end of a long wooden pew the day I visited the Prince George pub, and noticing two other wooden pews facing me from the opposite wall, I rather imagined I was sitting in a psychiatrist's waiting room. Most of the varnish had been scraped off the small table surface before me, and this, I deciphered, was undoubtedly the work of mad people.

I was in the rear left hand section of the bar, and on the wall to my left was a large *La Dolce Vita* movie poster featuring an image of a woman holding up a cat. On the wall beside it was a framed black and white photograph of another woman who was also holding up a cat. I had been pinned to a few bar walls myself, but only for short periods of time, and I found myself wishing I could somehow become a permanent fixture on the walls of the Prince George.

I looked for cats on my way back to the bar, and after ordering a drink from the psychiatrist, I told her about the dream I'd had where I was being chased by giant hair-curlers through an abandoned fairground and my legs were made out of spicy sausage meat. She nodded sympathetically before turning to another patron with raised eyebrows, and I gave them both my funny cross-eyed _expression before making my way back across the wooden floorboards, as if wearing large clown shoes. On the curdled cream wall opposite my table was a gigantic map of the world titled 'The World,' and various squat-like wooden bar stools were scattered around the waiting room area waiting patiently, I imagined, for the bums and arseholes of the likes of me. To my immediate left was a small black cupboard, which would have been no higher than three feet tall and rather narrow in width. I couldn't open it at first because my wooden pew was hard up against its door, so I began shunting the long bench seat along in order to create some space outside it.

I was the only one sitting in that area of the bar at the time, and no one noticed as I proceeded to pry the little door ajar before squatting down, climbing inside and pulling it shut again behind me. I sat hunched in the dark with my pint waiting for people to sit at the table outside, and I was cramped, of course, but there was a lovely musty smell from the encroaching walls, and it felt like night time even though it was the middle of the afternoon. I started making loud sucking noises to entertain myself, some of which were really, really funny, and at one point I laughed so much I coughed up some beer through my nose. While I was waiting, I heard the crash of pool balls coming from the toilets out back, and this noise intermingled with the echoing sounds of my own joints cracking. Eventually, after a couple of hours or so, I heard some footsteps and voices right outside the cupboard door announcing the arrival of some patrons at my table. They were talking about some interesting topic of the moment and they weren't scraping the varnish off the table surface or sounding particularly mad, so I knew I was pretty safe hiding inside a tiny cupboard right next to them. Wetting my lips, I began to play a few quiet chords from the harmonica I had managed to retrieve from my rear trouser pocket. I've never pretended to be a particularly accomplished harmonica player, and in fact all I really do is run my lips back and forth really fast and blow. A few strange sounds emerged, granted, and perhaps I wasn't as quiet as I had hoped to be either, but I think I pulled off a fairly convincing interpretation of 'Rhythm is a Dancer.'

A subsequent hush had emerged from the people immediately outside my tiny enclosed cupboard space, and when the little door was suddenly whisked back, I was temporarily blinded by the bright daylight that flooded the interior of the Prince George pub. After passing the interesting brown wall-mounted jukebox to the right of the entranceway, I was escorted out the main doors, meowing desperately in a last ditch attempt to find a cat I could be photographed with.

Prince George, Hackney E8 3AG

Surprise in Chelsea, Chelsea

This pub is in a very nice and pretty neighbourhood area and as I made my way along the pleasant streets a couple of dogs barked sharply at me. My nerves aren't what they used to be, but I managed to smile faintly and whisper back, 'Hey friends, you smell good too!' A collection of elderly people was sitting outside under umbrellas when I arrived at the Surprise, and I smiled warmly at them, politely tipping my imaginary peaked cap. Rather than joining them outside for some very fast drinking however, I decided to explore the lovely bar interior and soak in the warm atmosphere. I took my beer from the most pleasant barman with a knowing nod and opted for a rather large armchair in a red-carpeted back-room area to the right of the bar.

In front of my seat was a very small wooden table with a large round black ashtray centrally positioned, and on the walls were various works of art and their associated tags with explanatory titles, sizes and prices. Although my table was wooden and small, my armchair was in fact soft and huge, and it was upholstered in a flower-patterned light green. As soon as I sat down, I felt like I was drowning in the chair and my small arse disappeared somewhere below and my arms started flailing around like a person attempting to direct a large aeroplane to its parking grid. I tried to reach for my beer, but I simply sunk further into the light green, flower-pattered upholstery, and it dawned on me that I was, perhaps, in dire danger. Fortunately, just then a very sweet older woman on her way to the Ladies heard my cries and whimpers and my loud sucking noises, and lent me a frail old arm to assist in my recovery. Well, I should tell you that I'm not a large or strong man, and in fact I'm very much neither of these things, but despite this and despite the dear old madam's best intentions, well I quite simply yanked her right off her ruby red heels and onto the waves of light green, patterned flower cushioned upholstery. She squealed in an old fashioned way as the two of us rocked and swayed and buckled in the huge old chair, and I looked desperately across to the small table and my unattainable glass of beer, which was slowly dripping condensation like my red and furrowed brow. A bony elbow struck me in the face and for a minute the rustic red walls became a blur as my saviour of sorts floundered around above me, crying and screaming and cursing, while above us a very small chandelier type light-fitting flickered electrical flashes in all of its five droplet-shaped bulbs. Things were becoming desperate.

I needed to drink fluids, while my bucking, talcum-smelling passenger clearly needed to dispense with them. Another old woman clearly needed to also, as she too fortunately passed us on her path for the Ladies, stopping aghast with a vein laden hand across her mouth at the sight of myself and the first good lady floundering in the huge armchair. 'Help me!' cried my bony-elbowed old woman of good intention, thrusting her hand out to the other woman who was only slightly in less need of a pee than her good self. Well, wouldn't you know it? This second good Samaritan was thus hoisted afloat the turbulent waves of back room upholstery, with me pinned, punctured and drowning beneath the pair of them, and now well in need of a bladder deposit myself. With three of us now riding the perilous spring cushioned waves, there was clearly a commotion ensuing that would reach the ears of those patrons out front. Sure enough, a small army of people, comprising regular customers, bar staff and large husbands and sons quickly emerged to find two exceptionally well-respected old women of the community being tossed and turned above a churning tide of young, small drunken man and light green flower-patterned upholstered springy sofa chair.

In retrospect, I should have sat near the front of this great pub, where the lower windowpanes are stained in lovely green shades, the Gents are closer to hand, a Bar Billiards table is nearby, and the seats are sturdy wooden chairs with tables at a sensible height. Anyway, strong, hairy hands replaced the frail, bony arms of my two lovely old shipwreck companions, and these roughly scooped me out of the cushioned waves and thrust me out of the bar onto the clean hard street, where snarling, drooling dogs wet my jeans slightly before I could.

Surprise in Chelsea, Chelsea SW3 4AJ

SLIMY POPE

Tom Bradley

Originally Published: 2005

Rome's being closed to wheeled traffic in the daylight hours for the first time since Alaric sacked the place. Sitting here watching it on television, I have figured something out. It's about power, prophylactics, and the Pope. I suddenly understand what seduces public figures, what possesses them to make themselves over and set themselves up just like the golden calf that pissed Moses off so bad after he returned from his hike on Horeb.

I begin to understand the groin-tickling sensations that motivated John Paul—John Paul, that balding, husky darling of the airwaves. One of history's greatest criminals, this guy donned his triple tiara, cross-dressed in his silks and satins, and flaunted himself in front of overcrowded, starving, AIDS-ravished communities, holding up two plump fingers in a meretricious salute, and announcing that simple cream-bags were mortal abominations. It was like walking into a burning orphanage, telling the kids to stand on one leg until they'd learned better than to play with matches, and jacking off on their faces to cool the blisters as they formed.

That applause-ravenous Polack was the reason I never emerged from the car on Sunday mornings. Even on Easter and Christmas—the two days per year when my devout wife steeled herself and held over my head the threat of papally-dispensed annulment to get me into the Real Presence—I could never remain quietly seated in the family pew at that certain point in the service when the priest, our local attorney of nothingness, asked the congregation to say a little prayer in their hearts for the Holy Father in Rome.

PRETTY AUTHORS MAKE GRAVES

Steve Almond

Originally Published: 2005

There's a helluva lot more of us, than there is of them.
—Frank Zappa

I was an ugly kid. Buck teeth. Fat cheeks. Bad hair. Terrible hair. You look at the old albums and it's a museum of bad hair. I should have had myself shellacked. Maybe I was shellacked. I don't even remember.

But listen: most of the good writers out there are ugly. Butt ugly. Plug ugly. Fugly. I'd give you a long list of examples, but this isn't that kind of thing. I'm not interested in research. Research bores me. You know what I'm talking about, anyway. All that literary dogmeat. Except for Faulkner. Faulkner was hot. But he was a drunk.

I only trust the ugly writers, anyway. Deep down,

those are the ones who have earned their wrath. All the rest of them, the pretty boy and girl authors, screw them. Or, better yet, don't screw them. Get them all hot and bothered. Tell them you know Terry Gross, you once dated her former personal assistant, and then leave them there, lathered up, grinning, in a hot cloud of their own fabulous bone structure.

As for author photos, they're a goddamn fraud. The photo on my first book is Exhibit A. It's the most pathetic sensitivo-beefcake shot of the century. My friends tell me I look like a gay porn star. Maybe I am a gay porn star. Maybe my gay porn star name is Maxi Spray. Doesn't matter. Anyone who's seen me in person knows the truth. Fugly.

And what's not to be Fugly about? If you want to make art in this culture, if you want to shake people down for their feelings, you're ugly by proxy anyway. All that's going to happen is this: you'll sit down and decide you're profound and you'll write a lot of dreck for a long time and various people along the way will feed you little niblets of praise, which you deserve, but not for what you're actually writing, which is still a stinking heap of narcissism. Then, eventually, you'll start to send your work out to the bad parents of the world and they'll find it (and you) ugly and send you little slips of paper with passive-aggressive inscriptions printed by machines and you'll start to see yourself, finally, as they do: an ugly little wannabe freak with no business card and a car that makes guys stop you in the parking lot of your supermarket and offer body work for cheap. This is called progress.

Because what you're aiming for here is to rediscover that inconsolably ugly little kid inside you, because that's what triggers the beauty jones.

Some measures that will help:

1. Watch a lot of television—Television is the place where you will realize that beauty makes people stupid. If you keep watching for long enough, it will dawn on you that the opposite is just as true.

2. Read the Bible—Not the whole thing, just enough to figure out the basic point: that God's toughest gig is to love the ugly.

3. Stop exercising—Two key words for you here are Restless and Flabby. Pasty is also of considerable import.

4. Stay away from healthy romantic interaction— The worst thing you can do, actually, is to use the funk of sexual success as a hedge against the appropriate depths of self-horror. Remember: you're probably clever enough to fool someone better looking for a while. But in the end, you're ugly. That's where you live, and you live there alone.

The rest (bad news!) consists of the dogged, lonely work. You sit there. You push your characters around. And when you, or they, feel ugly enough, have felt ugly enough for long enough, a little thrush of beauty unfurls to rescue both of you. Then it disappears.

If you're truly unlucky, some of the bad parents out there will start to accept your crap and you'll move on to the next set of bad parents until finally you're dealing with the world of New York Publishing, which is inhabited by bright, ambitious people who hate your guts for still trying. They will make you feel worse and worse and uglier and uglier and in the end you'll need to thank them, because they, too, are helping you find that inner ugly schmuck kid I keep mentioning.

I use the italics, though, because it is perfectly reasonable to fantasize about punching these asswipes for years and years, because that is precisely what they deserve. They deserve to be punched. But they are only emissaries from the world of commerce, bit players, pimps and petty tyrants, and they have only the numbers to defend them, which is to say, they have no defence, whereas all of us, the artists, we have our ugliness and the resultant beauty pinned to our lapels.

Are you picking up what I'm putting down?

Let me tell you a little story.

When I was in seventh grade I fell in with a crowd of pretty people. At my school, they were called rah rahs. They were viewed with derision by the rest of the population, who were either physically ugly or wrongly colored or suffered from the ultimate form of disfigurement, which, in this culture, is poverty.

I myself was plain ugly, but I'd gone to a grade school that nobody recognized and so I was a novelty and eager to please and, as such, was adopted by the rah rahs. There was one girl in particular, Nicole Taylor, and she was absolutely stunning: blond hair, blue eyes, sky jump nose, just what you'd expect. She was also—and I'm not sure why I'm mentioning this, but it seems obscurely relevant—a Mormon.

One night, we were at a party up in Los Altos Hills, the wealthy part of town, and we started playing spin the bottle. Nicole spun the bottle and it landed on me. I was absolutely terrified. She knee-walked over to me and she set her lips to mine and stuck her tongue out. What I'm telling you: she pried my mouth open with her hard little tongue and jabbed it around once or twice and then she pulled away from me and returned to her place with an expression of icy disgust.

She never forgave me for that indignity, which was the indignity of the beautiful having to embrace the ugly. And yet she remained strangely fascinated by me. She couldn't understand why I was a part of her clique. It offended her strict sense of social and aesthetic order. More so: she simply couldn't understand how I could persist in my ugliness, how I got along in the world with no shell of beauty to protect me. This threatened her terribly.

At a party some months later, at her own lavish home, I and a kid named Troy took part in an impromptu chugalug contest. Troy was as boring as a stump, but he was also the most handsome boy in the history of the world. He was so handsome you wanted to lick his skin. So we chugged our bottles of Sprite and let the carbonation burn our throats and suddenly Nicole appeared in front of us and said:

Steve Almond, if you spit that soda on me I'll have my boyfriend kick your ass!

I spit the soda on her.

I didn't mean to. It was a reflex move. Nicole burst into tears. She spent the rest of the party in a state of puffy bereavement, while I cowered about and everyone else shook their heads. Nicole got what she wanted: I was neatly expelled from the rah rahs.

The lesson is this: justice can be its own form of beauty. And this: the ugly are doomed to a certain kind of solitude. Alright, fine. What else is the life of a writer? We're all frauds waiting to be found out. We're all cowering dogs. We're all hoping to wring a little beauty from the neck of shame. Fine. Fine fine fine.

Let me tell you another story.

When I was in tenth grade I went to see a play at the local high school auditorium. It was a play about Vietnam, something righteous and tragic. I got there late, so I had to sit in the front row. (Do I need to tell you that I came alone? That I could not find anyone to accompany me?) Just at the end of the second act, during the big, tense soliloquy by the star—who was supposed to be ugly, disfigured by the war, but was, in fact, as handsome as James Dean—I cut a fart. It wasn't a very loud fart. Just a quiet little fart that slipped out. But it came during one of those hushed, actorly pauses and it caused the people sitting in the front three rows to start laughing, softly and incontrovertibly. And when the lights went up I hurried from the theater and went to get my bike from the racks and I heard a bunch of kids behind me laughing.

When I turned around they stopped abruptly and one of them, a nice, sort of homely girl named Kendall, came over and asked me how I was doing. She felt bad for me. I was The Boy Who Farted. For the rest of high school, I would be The Boy Who Farted. I would be renowned, in the small, merciless universe of my high school, for having let a little cloud of ugliness escape my body in public.

When people ask me how I came to write and why I write so much and why there's such an embarrassing yearning for beauty in the shit I write, I often feel like telling them this story. Asking them: what would you do if you were The Boy Who Farted? Wouldn't you want to convince the world to regard you in some more flattering light?

A few more items of business:

Buy art, okay? Quit mucking about like a cheapskate and wolfing down burgers from Fat Food. Stop throwing your money down Hollywood's sewers. Vote with your dough and vote for the stuff written or sculpted or filmed by the ugly. Actually concentrate on who you're having sex with. Hold your one and only heart to a higher standard. And so on.

I'm proud to be ugly, and proud to make pretty things.

What are you?

NOT JESUS YET

Steven Hall

Originally Published: 2005

The green room is green. Like the inside of a plant. Green green green. Walls, furniture, fish tanks, fish, pinball machines and carpets; everything in the green room of my house is exactly the same shade of—oh my god, you're so meticulous Harrison—green. It's the next day and I'm walking with Barry down the corridor towards it.

'But I need to know something, give me something.'

'No you don't.'

'No? No I don't? How can you possibly think that, Harrison? How can it occur as a possibility in your head that I wouldn't need to know —' I'm walking into the green room and Barry is close up behind me. '—what it is I'm supposed to be promoting? You do still need promoting; I hope you're aware of that fact, Harrison. You're not Jesus yet. Not yet you're not.'

'Jesus,' I say the word slowly, then: 'Calm down.'

'I am calm. I am the epitome of fucking serenity.' Barry puts a sweet that might be a bonbon into his mouth. 'I just need a bit of support with this. Don't go dropping this shit all over me, not after everything with that fuckhole Thomas. I'm not exactly A1 at the moment, Harrison, or haven't you noticed?'

'There is no shit,' I say and I pour Barry a green drink from the green bar. 'And even if there was any shit I don't think any of it would be dropping all over you.' I hand him the glass and Barry sticks his nose into it.

'What the fuck is this?'

'Vodka.'

'Green vodka.'

'Green vodka.'

Barry tries some of it then rattles the glass from side to side with his eyebrows up at me. I don't really know or care what this might mean.

'Look HB,' he says. 'I understand what you want to do with this, honestly, I really do. Big fucking unveiling and all the press coverage with the 'world waits with baited breath for the new Slashmodern masterpiece' angle. I get it. I get it and I love it. But, stop me and fucking buy one, I need to know something, just something so I can field this thing.'

I sit on the edge of a barstool and hold my glass of vodka against the wood to check that both are the exact same shade of green. They are. I knew that already.

'You will see it,' I say, 'when there is something to see.'

'Jesus!'

'Not yet.' I don't move. 'It's sensitive Barry. If anyone finds out about the work before it happens then it might not happen at all. Can you understand? You'd be promoting an artwork that'd given itself a big fucking abortion.'

'Fucking shit!' Barry is on his feet and rubbing his hands through his hair and across his head and it's a similar thing to what people do with balloons when they are trying to make them stick to the ceiling. 'That's it isn't it? That's it!'

'What?'

'A big fucking abortion! Man, oh man, that's fantastic. I knew you'd tell me, I knew you'd fucking crack. A fucking abortion... Jesus.'

'The work is not going to be an abortion Barry,' I say slowly. 'That isn't what I meant.'

Barry looks like the air is coming out of him from somewhere and I think maybe the pills he's taking are not doing the same job they used to [get some better pills Barry].

'I tell you what though,' he says, rubbing his chin after a minute. 'It isn't a bad idea is it?'

I think about this. 'No,' I say. 'It isn't a bad idea.'

Barry talks about abortion as art for a few more minutes and I'm sort of interested in what he's saying and I'm thinking yeah maybe but then a nail sticks into my leg and draws blood. I bend down to look at the nail and it is bent and jutting out of the bar and a kind of iron grey, not green. My leg is bleeding and the blood is red, not green either.

'Marci,' I shout, still looking at the nail. 'Can you come in here?'

Marci appears in a green apron. 'Yes, Mr. Brodie?'

I straighten up and turn to face her. 'Has Duchamp been in here?'

'I'm not sure...'

'Marci,' I say. 'Don't cover for him. Who else hammers nails into the bar?'

'I think Roy only left him for...'

'Right.'

'It's just that...'

'Duchamp is spoiled,' I say. 'Gala luncheons, the media, the critics.' I point to the grey nail, and then to the red blood on my leg. 'I don't like it when this happens.'

'Well, perhaps if you were to speak to him, Mr Brodie.'

'We agreed that I'm not going to speak to him until he apologises for what he did to Barry.' And as I say this Barry reaches up to touch the side of his face where I can still make out the faint bruise even though Barry is wearing make-up to conceal it.

'It's nothing Harrison, honestly,' he says.

'It is,' I say, 'something.'

And then there's silence.

'Actually,' Barry jumps back up to speed like he has a kick-start, 'I need to talk to you about Duchamp too, about his exhibition.'

'About...' I say, sort of listening but more staring at the grey nail and the red blood again. 'Marci, can something be done about this?'

'Yes Mr. Brodie.'

I turn to Barry, 'What about his exhibition? Do you not ever, I don't know, think it's—odd?'

'What? Odd? Look, you can't hold him back Harrison, you really can't. Not when he's going to be received like this. Duchamp is on the brink of international recognition is his own right. Fucking Christ, not even I have any idea how big this will—'

'Barry,' I say. 'Duchamp is a monkey.'

'But the world, Harrison, the world are going to love him and he's going to be—'

'Monkey,' I say. 'He. Is. A. Monkey.'

'Harrison, do I look to you like the kind of fuck who doesn't know a monkey when he sees one? Of course Duchamp is a monkey. I am well aware of that fact HB and that's exactly what makes him so... so—'

'Hairy.'

'Gifted Harrison, gifted. His work, it's so raw, so primitive. Duchamp puts people in touch with something old and primal, something that came before —' a sweep of the arm '— all this.' Barry looks at me. 'Are you all right?'

'Puts people in touch with,' I say slowly, thinking out loud, but not about Duchamp. Was there, is there, more to that than just the five words? Maybe—what?

A ghost of something? People in with touch puts. In with people puts touch. I swap the words around in my head quickly, chasing a fading shadow of resonance. With puts touch people in. Touch puts with people in. But—no. It's gone. If it was ever there in the first place. There is a fly in the green room high up around the green lamp and I watch it turning lazy circles. The fly isn't green either. I let my eyes slowly fall from the fly to Barry. 'Lost it,' I say.

'What?' asks Barry, bringing his eyebrows together.

I rub my eyes to clear my brain.

'Sorry,' I say.

'Duchamp,' says Barry. 'Forthcoming exhibition,' says Barry. 'Get with the program,' says Barry.

'Okay,' I say. 'Right. Duchamp likes to hammer nails into things. Just that.'

'And?'

With people in puts touch. People with puts touch in.

'Harrison?'

People touch—fuck. 'Forget it,' I say. 'It's gone.'

'Okay, look. The monkey is going to make it big so...' I get up on Barry's 'so' and head out of the room and Barry grabs his glass and follows me. 'Alright alright, Jesus, we can discuss the monkey later. We still have a two month window with NYC, so, providing he's being productive—'

'Duchamp is being productive,' I say, walking. 'I'm excited by his new direction. I think he's moving into etching.'

227

'You know what?' Barry's voice from behind. 'That doesn't suit you. Sarcasm I mean. People expect more.'

'What people?'

'You know, people.'

'Right,' I say. 'Good,' I say.

'So,' says Barry, I still can't see him because he's behind me. 'Are you going to tell me about your Slashmodernism Prize entry or not, because, let me tell you, if you're thinking —'

The corridor leads from the green room to the purple room, which contains amongst other things, two big sofas separated by a glass table, all perfectly purple.

Mcaffery had a glass table by the artist Image Incomatsou which was really a Japanese man on all fours balancing the sheet of glass on his back all day. You have to keep buying the work, Mcaffery's agent said once, probably to Barry, it's never really yours. But Mcaffery's agent sold the table anyway, because it would always spill Mcaffery's drinks and nobody else's and so to teach it a lesson Mcaffery was going to put a four gallon fish tank on it and also some heavy books.

Barry is still talking about the importance of him getting an angle—'Why would you fucking shut me out on this, Harrison?'—and I really can't be arsed to go through the whole thing with him again because he won't listen so I just drop onto one of the sofas, drain my glass of green vodka and go to top up with purple liquid from a handy decanter.

'Want some?' I ask, and I'm waving the decanter at Barry and cutting him off midway through the necessity of advanced and targeted networking.

'What? What is it?'

I sniff my glass and it's not a bad question.

'Marci.' She appears in seconds, wearing a purple apron. 'Marci. What is this?'

'It's whisky Mr. Brodie.'

'Whisky,' I say to Barry. 'It's whisky.'

'Purple whisky?'

'Yes.'

'Right,' Barry thinks. 'Yeah, why not?'

I pour Barry a drink and start with questions, probably to keep him distracted from the Slashmodernism Prize.

'Barry, am I interested in environmental issues?'

Barry takes a sip of his scotch and thinks. 'No,' he says. 'Environmental issues are exactly what you and other young men of your generation should be interested in and therefore you generate more heat if you are not interested in them. Why?' he asks. 'Are you interested in them?'

'I don't know,' I say. 'Do I have a girlfriend at the moment?'

'Official or unofficial?'

'Either.'

Every two weeks the TV channel Exploration 7 shows a cheap documentary about how if you're standing at the other end of the universe with a big telescope you can actually see the American Civil War. And there's another one they show late at night about how tiny particles in laboratories do unlikely things depending on how scientists with beards look at them or sometimes worry them with expensive tools. Watching this kind of TV and knowing Barry both make answering questions like do you have a girlfriend difficult.

'It's possible,' Barry says after a minute.

I take a long sip of my purple scotch then start swirling the liquid around the walls of the glass.

'Have I got over Miranda's death yet?'

Barry puts his drink down onto the table as though he's thinking about this, but Barry does a lot of things as though he's thinking about them.

'Well, yes and no,' he says. 'You still miss her a great deal but you have decided to move on and get on with things because that's what she would have wanted. You don't like to talk about her death or the last few months of her life any more. Why? Officially, because you find it too difficult and unofficially and more fucking importantly we've done the angle and there is nothing more to be gained in having you continually connected to eating disorders and all that depressing teen body angst bullshit.'

'Right,' I say and I'm nodding, 'got it. How long was I 'in mourning' or whatever?'

'Well,' Barry says, 'you'll like this. We tell people that you were 'deeply troubled'—we don't say mourning, Harrison—for six months after Miranda's death and everyone buys it up now, but—and this is the good bit—we had some good luck with news and sports fixtures and that toddler was abducted if you remember, so we only had to take you out of circulation for two and a half months and in the meantime everyone lost track and so when the papers came back to us we passed it off like it was forever. After a while we'll be able to say it was fucking years before you got yourself back on track again because people don't remember this kind of shit and it'll be a great angle for your past.' Barry looks very pleased with himself. 'Just tell me. How good am I HB?'

'You're the best Barry,' I tell him. 'So, do I get emotional about it publicly? Like every so often or anything?'

'Hmmm,' says Barry. 'Maybe,' says Barry. 'That's a tricky one,' says Barry.

I look down into my glass and I see the reflection of my own eye looking back up at me, a purple oval and lens staring through liquid rings of movement. I blink and it blinks and it seems no more or less alien than anything else at the moment. I have the word Normality printed in dark grey on dark grey card pinned up in my office and the word is completely invisible.

'Decide and get back to me,' I say, then looking up: 'What do I think of the big corporations? What do I think of Core Enterprises and the others?'

'That's straightforward,' Barry says. 'You'll love every last one of them if they'll fucking pay.'

I say 'that would make sense,' but I'm distracted because maybe that ghost of something, that meaning or whatever is here again, summoned up by—I don't know what this time, but anyway, as soon as I notice it, it's gone.

THE MISSING KIDNEY

Ben Myers

Originally Published: 2005

Assembly Announcement

1988. The day of the operation they prayed for me in assembly. Prayed for me, right there between an educational anecdote about a boy who pretends to be Bobby Charlton's nephew and the usual: announcements (congratulations to Gary Tibbs in fourth form for breaking his opponent's arm in the judo junior nationals at the weekend, maintenance in the art block, all first and second year pupils no longer allowed to hang round the shopping precinct at lunch time, two pupils suspended for smoking weed).

What madness. Praying for me.

I didn't find out about it until years later, when a friend a couple of years older than me who I didn't happen to get to know until after we'd left school, happened to mention it one time. Didn't you die during an operation or something?

Not quite.

No doubt most of the pupils didn't have a clue who I was, and why would they?

A nice thought though. A nice thought for kidney boy.

Counting Backwards From 10

'I want you to relax, and then count down backwards from 10.'

She slipped the needle into my vein and fiddled with some dials on the machine.

'From ten?'

'Yes.'

'OK. Can I just ask a quick question?'

'Of course—but you better make it quick.'

'Does it have to be from 10 for scientific purposes, or is it for more random reasons?'

I felt a pleasant warmth spread throughout my body. It was like being injected with treacle and everything slowed down and took on the agreeable hue of the most beautiful sunset you've seen. Or sunrise. Either/or.

'It's just random, really. People never make it to 10—at least not if I'm doing my job correctly anyway!'

She laughed at this, silently, but with a vigour that involved her entire body. She laughed like a tar whirlpool.

'OK, you better start counting now.'

'T…'

I was out.

Gone. Immobilised.

The last thing I remember is grasping for the tip of an iceberg marked 'Ten' as it slowly drifted further and further away, melting as it did so under those warming rays of lights that beamed down from above.

'Ten' was the kidney and it would not return.

Kidney Myths Of New Orleans

The following statement was released via the New Orleans Police on January 30 1997 after they were inundated by calls from members of the public—many of them in town for Mardi Gras—concerning supposed stories of business travellers awakening up in bath tubs full of ice in New Orleans hotel rooms, with only a telephone and note saying 'call 911' for company.

Over the past six months the New Orleans Police Department has received numerous inquiries from corporations and organizations around the United States warning travelers about a well organized crime ring operating in New Orleans. This information alleges that this ring steals kidneys from travelers, after they have been provided alcohol to the point of unconsciousness.

After an investigation into these allegations, the New Orleans Police Department has found them to be COMPLETELY WITHOUT MERIT AND WITHOUT FOUNDATION. The warnings that are being disseminated through the Internet are FICTITIOUS and may be in violation of criminal statutes concerning the issuance of erroneous and misleading information.

Any organization wishing to speak with members of the New Orleans Police Department is asked to contact Lieutenant Marlon Defillo, Office of Public Affairs at (504) 826-2828

—New Orleans Police

Human beings are very good at passing around such stories until what was once subject to outside forces like change, opinion and conjecture the edges become smoothed away and it turns into a solid, irrefutable object of truth, like a pebble that has ridden the Tsunami of time all the way into the shore.

The setting and the main characters may differ, but the story remains the same: man wakes up without kidneys, but has plenty of ice for his drinks.

Or, the more concise version: never drink with surgeons.

And at this point, the genesis of the tale becomes irrelevant. It is now urban myth, something that is far more interesting than the truth, which actually looks kind of jagged and dirty and not all crafted by the tides of the social sea.

Urban myths reflect the imagination of the culture—like a kidney they filter out the waste and impurities of the subject and get down to the raw basics, even if you have to put in a whole load of external influences or stimuli in there first. All of which is really just a strange way of saying that to find the truth sometimes to you have to fictionalise it.

So though no-one on is on record as having woken in that old time voodoo town New Orleans without their kidneys, it doesn't mean it's untrue.

Just because a kidney doesn't go missing somewhere, doesn't mean no kidneys have gone missing anywhere.

The Boy Who Cycled Into A House

I opened my eyes and there was a boy in the bed next to me. Previously it had been empty, though everyone knows hospital beds don't stay empty for long. No matter how quickly they patched people up and sent them on their way, they just kept coming with their cuts and burns and breaks and mystery illnesses.

The boy was a couple of years older than me with a thick mop of hair. He was dark in the way kids who run carefree through fields and streams and housing estates are dark, though I knew it was as much down to poverty and a lack of parental responsibility. He sat up on bed, topless, looking perfectly at ease. He had the unself-conscious look of someone who was used to not wearing a T-shirt anyway

'What are you in for?' he asked, like we were two old lags coming together in a cell of our own physical making.

'Kidney,' I said.

'Shame,' he said, breezily.

Neither of us said anything for a minute or two, then he spoke.

'Me, I cycled into a house. It was a choice between this car that was, like, speeding towards me or the side of a house. I chose the house.'

'I think you made the right choice.'

'Perhaps. Though I was knocked out and woke up here in hospital listening to you moaning and groaning, so who's to say?'

'Maybe if you'd made the other choice it would have been a lot worse.'

'Maybe. They told me that the bike was bent double so what the hell am I supposed to do now?'

I imagined this boy's bike, bent in half lying on a

pavement somewhere, one wheel still spinning as the ambulance departs and the crowd disperses. No one is sure what do about the bike, so they just leave it lying there.

The wheel stops spinning and the bike looks dead and useless, a tangle of metal and scraped paintwork that's of no use to anyone. Nobody wants to take responsibility for the bike because they know it's ruined, but all the same, maybe someone should put it aside in case it's of sentimental value to the boy, which all bikes are to all children. But no-one does anything except go into their homes or drive off or continue serving customers in the newsagent across the road, the same shop that sold the boy sweets this morning.

The image of the abandoned bike is the saddest thing in the world. Night falls, and the temperature falls. At some point some kids younger than the bike's owner come along and stand around the bike. It's pretty late, but it was one of those areas. The parents don't care much about what their kids do; they gave up contributing to the world long before they had even given birth to them.

One of the kids kicks the bike and the wheel spins again. They discuss whether it's worth salvaging, then decide against it so they kick and stomp the bike, then snap the spokes off the wheel and run off, hitting each other with them.

Early the next morning someone will remove the seat and someone else will make a half-hearted attempt to remove the tyres, but abandon it half through, bored or hungry, no doubt.

By lunch time tomorrow the husk of the bike will have been kicked into the road, then finally moved out of the way by a man in a delivery van, who had the rare distinction of having never learned how to ride the bike due to a bout of childhood polio.

Nevertheless, sitting here now the boy appeared to be very philosophical about it all, maybe because he hadn't seen the same sad abandoned bike scene that I could.

He also seemed like a pro at this patient business, a point confirmed to me when the Sister said 'Oh, back again Darren?' and he just grinned beneath his dirt and hair. Maybe he knew what he was thinking because then he said:

'I've been in here before. They all know me.'

'What for?'

'One time for a broken arm, another when I fell out of a tree and knocked myself out. Once when I cut my leg open on some broken glass. Oh, and once when my cousin beat me with a bike chain. Wait a second,' he said, reaching for the plastic bottle on his bed-side table. 'I've got to piss.'

He put the bottle under his sheets, settled back and began to piss, the glow of relief and relaxation spreading across his face. He looked like the most content person in the world

'I'm going to be a stunt man when I'm older,' he said.

Hare-Lip Holiday

After I'd been in hospital for what seemed like an aeon but was actually only about half that, and was hard at work resting at home, it was decided by my parents that they would take me away for a couple of days. Reasoning that sea-air was always historically associated with convalescence and recovery, and a seaside holiday would compensate for spending most of the summer holidays on my back in a ward with little in the way of ventilation and a very loud television, my dad hitched up the caravan and drove us south to Scarborough.

Scarborough got its name from two Icelandic Vikings, Thorgills and Kormak Ogmundarson. They were two bad boy brothers. In 966, having determined to single-handedly attempt to write the Sagas with fists and hatchets alone they stocked up their boat and, with a small army of strong blond Icelanders, left their homeland behind in search of adventure and bounty. They undertook a series of show-no-mercy raids on the coast of Britain. Soon they had established a particular stronghold in a dramatic sweep of conjoined bays backed by green slopes on Yorkshire's East coast, which they named 'Skarthaborg', a variation of Thorgills' nickname 'Skarthi's Burg', meaning 'hare lip'.

Thorgills had been born that way and it had only served to make him a better Viking. All the childhood teasing had made him bitter, angry and violent—perfect warrior material. Just wind him up and watch him go, the other Vikings used to say, and then laugh from deep within their whale-skins. Sometimes you just had to look at Thorgills the wrong way and he'd skin you.

At 'Hare Lip' they enjoyed good fishing and good rutting with those local women who had not managed to flee the area in time. Like I said, bad boys. They didn't need an invitation. Soon they were breeding and a stronghold grew into community into a fading holiday resort. The fading bit was a relatively recent addition.

This took many centuries of conflict and dispute and set-backs but this is no place to tell that tale. This is a book about a missing kidney, goddammit.

And that's how I found myself resting and recuperating in a caravan on a hare-lip that sat below the nose of a vicious Viking warrior, and the hare-lip was trying to smile but it just sort of twisted into a weird geographical grimace of cliff-face that followed the coast line, perfectly parallel to a flight path of many screaming seagulls who also had just enjoyed some good fishing well over one thousand years after the Ogmundarsons first salted a cod there and Thorgills brained Bjarni Sigmundsson with a rusty oar-lock for calling him Skarthi's Burg a little too sarcastically.

Half-Man, Half-Coal Mine

There's a sauna I frequent whenever I'm back in the town that took my kidney and paraded it through the streets of my imagination like a returning war hero.

The sauna is the domain of the miners. Or, the ex-miners, for the heart of that industry was ripped out and not given a hero's welcome. Instead it was thrown in the dirt and stomped on by some mad old woman, who then lifted her M&S skirts, squatted and pissed on it, steaming in the northern soil. Then, just to be sure, she cut the throat of the body from which it came.

No matter how long they shower or many hours they pass in the steam room or sweating it out in the pine-lined sweat box, the miners always seem to glisten within an unseen layer of local history. It's like no matter what they do or how long they've been retired, they spent so long underground that they gradually become at one with it.

They are all in their sixties, naked, their cock and balls hanging like intricate mechanisms. Some are skinny, others carry their pot bellies before them as if they were crates of glass bottles, clinking empties brought up from the cellar. They look like normal once-working men now relaxing into their old age, but I know they are each half-man, half-coal mine.

Their father and their father's father were miners before them. And before them, their father's father's father, and his father too. And on and on, a line of fathers standing at the mouth of a pit tunnel, new born baby in his arms, who they each gently streak with coal dust and say 'This is what will be' too. Centuries of tunnelling and digging and shunting, and nightly tin baths in their subsidised home has shaped them into a new breed. A dying breed. All they know and have ever known is earth and industry; a trade to pull them through the darkest hours, little realising they were no different to the canaries the mine owners also employed. Hours in the darkness with the dirt digging deep into the soul of it all until coal and flesh began to meld and contort until each became something else, half-man, half coal mine.

Many of them are called Ralph—pronounced 'Rarf', round here.

But now the mine is closed and the line is over. These miners of today—their sons won't be able to tell the tale of their fathers' fathers. They'll do something else, like demolition work or web design. They're the last of the breed, the half-men, half-coal mines.

Though their every conversation is entrenched in mining culture, they don't seem too bitter. Their bloodline had been cut but they weren't going to let that spoil things, not when there's a sauna as hot as Hades and a special weekday reduction for pensioned miners.

I sit in there, up on a shelf, listening as one rises to ladle iced water onto the hot coals, then sits himself back down. Another tells a dirty joke and they all laugh. All except one, who they call a 'miserable get' but he just ignores them then launches into a long-winded anecdote about a belt he bought in Spain, and even though they roll their eyes still join in to share their own accounts of international travel.

Though they are the last of a breed, they were also the first. Before them no other half-man, half-mine had holidayed on the Med before. Those opportunities hadn't been available until the boomtime of commercial airlines and worldwide travel agencies on every high street that came in the '60s and '70s.

It would be funny to turn and look at the poolside lounger on the left and see a half-man, half coal-mine rubbing suntan oil into his pulleys and dust-carts. Well, you'd probably blink and then look again. And if you were brash and insensitive you might shout 'Hey, look over here! It's one of those half-man, half coal mine's I read about. No way!' and perhaps a crowd would gather around him, blocking the rays of sunlight that he'd hacked six tonnes of raw coal to lie under, and look at him like suddenly Spain was a circus and he was the freak show.

They rarely speak to me, which is fine. I go to the sauna to sweat lots, not for the conversation. After ten minutes in there even breathing becomes hard work; there is no room left in the lungs for anecdotes.

This one time though, one of them did ask me about my scar.

'Where'd you get that, lad?'

'From a kidney operation. I had it removed.'

'So did I,' he said and pointed to his waist where a

scar disguised as a crease in the ripples of flesh made himself known, like it had been hiding there in the world's longest game of hide and seek, but was now bored and hungry.

And he had, and we both laughed, and neither of us felt like we needed to add anything else to add to the conversation. Two scars sitting there side by side. We knew.

WHEN LIBIDO RAN WILD

Bruce Benderson

Originally Published: 2005

To You, My Readers:

Contrary to what some deranged gay activists are now saying, the only thing the word "gay" refers to is what you do with your dick and your mouth and your asshole. Otherwise we guys who fuck asses and burp sperm eat the same foods you do. Our sphincters work the same as yours. We just know how to relax them when we want to.

But one thing about us that's a little bit different from the rest of you is our bars. A lot of you straight people go to bars to get drunk or watch baseball on television or sing karaoke or talk about books. We go to bars mostly to get our asses worked over. Sometimes we even suck cock right there in the bars. A good share of our bars have porn films playing right up there on the TV screen. We even have a few bars where we whip each other or lick each other's boots.

The last hot gay bar in New York disappeared in the late '90s right before Mayor Giuliani announced he had prostate cancer. While he was peeing radioactive pellets and slowly turning into a eunuch, his Gestapo was closing all the good hustler bars and all the good backroom bars and chasing every decent transvestite hooker from Times Square. So what's left to write about when it comes to literature and gay bars? Not a fucking thing. What's there to write about an endless throng of white faggots with gym bodies and shaved balls wearing tight tee shirts and dancing to mindless house music on Ecstasy? Not anything I can think of.

Unless I've missed something, there hasn't been one good book about fags and their bars for quite a few years now. That's a major break with tradition, since in generations past some of the best American litera-ture was written by horny faggots and their search for dick in New York's bars. Perhaps you're familiar with some of that classic dick-chasing literature to which I'm referring. In the 1950s, William Burroughs wrote about the search for dick in his ground breaking novel *Queer*, and in the early 60s John Rechy's novel *City of Night* followed a hot, alienated hustler through the streets, beds and bars of Times Square and the rest of the country.

I think we're getting to a theory here. When cock-sucking and ass-fucking were illegal activities, writers who couldn't get enough dick put themselves through all kinds of risks and dangers. So what they wrote about was inspired. Those were the days when gay bars could get raided. But when they didn't, they had good Mafia management who created a place where libido could run wild.

Don't believe the hype about the infamous Stonewall bar being an oppressive place where sad homosexuals had to hide from police oppression and where Mafia bosses exploited their desperation. Any illegal bar run by the Mafia always has the hottest, most inspiring atmosphere. And excitement, risk and underground activity are what makes the best writing. The Mafia may have created a lot of heartache in our cities, but we owe them a debt for having created such good illicit bars, which were at the basis of a lot of good American literature.

As for me, I probably wouldn't have written a decent sentence if I hadn't discovered Times Square and the hot Puerto Rican hustlers who came down from the South Bronx to frequent its mostly Mafia-owned bars. You see, the other ingredient of good literature is class "penetration". If you sit on your ass all day writing stories about infidelity at the local university, you'll end up like the poet of the American suburbs, John Updike. But those who write about encounters with other classes, other worlds have found the secret of exciting narratives. All the tensions of class encounters make for some fucking good reading.

The first and most famous Times Square bar I ever went to was called the Haymarket. It was a big, sprawling place on Eighth Avenue with cheap drinks, a long bar counter, booths you could sit in and a big pool table. In those days, a lot of the hustlers were poor white kids. Since the minimum drinking age in those days was 18 (rather than today's 21), there was some very young trade in there. The place was pulsing with young testosterone and horny old men willing to spend the $20 on some fresh meat.

One of the best novels about that scene was written by a guy named Paul Rogers. It's a novel called *Saul's Book*, which tells the story of an angelic but fucked-up Puerto Rican hustler-junkie and his Jewish john-daddy who is a reader of Shakespeare and a forger of checks. When the book was published around 1980, it won a prestigious literary prize called the Pushcart. Everybody thought that Paul Rogers was a social worker who had learned about that sleazy world of hustlers through his altruistic profession. It turned out, however, that Rogers was just like his character Saul. He was a drug addict and a con man with a taste for young trade. The love of his life—a fucked up white kid with a learning disability and a drug habit—eventually bludgeoned him to death. And Rogers was dead before he could even write a second novel.

One other very talented guy was linked to the Haymarket scene. There was Alan Bowne, who wrote the play *Forty Deuce*. "Forty Deuce" means Forty-Second Street in street lingo. The play got rave reviews on Broadway and was one of the first starring roles of a twenty-year-old Kevin Bacon. Later Paul Morrissey, of Warhol fame, made a magnificent movie of *Forty Deuce*, but the film was never released. *Forty Deuce* tells the story of a group of hustlers who end up with the corpse of a twelve-year old boy in the bed of the hotel room they use to turn tricks. They plot to pin the death on a very bourgeois john by slipping him angel dust. But there's a happy ending to the story.

When I came to Times Square, John Rechy, Paul Rogers and Alan Bowne had already paved the way for me and the books I would write about it. But let me make one thing clear. I didn't start hanging out in Times Square because I wanted to write about it. I guess only a journalist would do that. Those guys are used to picking a subject that will make them a few bucks whether they're inspired by it or not. No, I didn't go to Times Square to write. I went there cause I wanted to fuck straight guys.

You see, most of the hustlers in Times Square were straight. At this point, the majority were Puerto Rican. And they were very poor. Getting their dick sucked was a lot easier for some of them than robbery or drug dealing. They figured it was no big deal getting their cock sucked. I wish more of you straights were like that. All they had to do was stand there while some very experienced cocksucker gave them an ace blow job. It's true that some of them with fancy drug habits had to learn to suck dick themselves, but in general their performance wasn't very inspired.

I hope my readers can understand this concept. For a straight Latin or North African or other Mediterranean type sticking your cock in a guy's mouth or ass isn't considered gay. The only thing that makes you a faggot is if you yourself take it up the ass. O.K., some of them did, but they were high.

O'Neal's, on 48th Street, was the bar that took the place of the defunct Haymarket. It was a two-room affair with a little garden at the back. The manager was a handsome laid-back Greek named Alex. Murphy, a big bearded guy who looked like a Hell's Angel, and who'd been the bouncer at the old Stonewall, was at the door. Later somebody said he was a police informer. Now Murphy's gone. He died of AIDS.

Some of my best memories come from hanging out in O'Neal's in the mid-eighties. South Bronx hustlers, doctors and fashion designers, runaway kids, drag queens, drug dealers and the homeless all frequented the place. Around 1986, crack hit the streets. People were puffing on glass pipes (known as devil's dicks) in the garden at O'Neal's. There was a lot of brawling. One guy got gutted by a knife. I'll never forget the day this one gigantic hustler got mad cause he lost a pool game. He picked up one end of the pool table and overturned it. It went crashing through the plate glass doorway.

It was in O'Neal's that I first became fascinated with the speech and minds of street people. Sure I liked sucking their dicks, caressing their tattoos made in jail, kissing their scars and sleeping with them in my arms. But I was also trying to figure out what gave them their courage and coolness, what wisdom they had that none of us educated folks could ever master. After a while, I found myself imitating the way they talked, and that was when I began writing stories about them. Luckily, I was no idiot. I never lost sight of the fact that I came from a bourgeois background and could never think entirely like they did. So when I wrote fiction about Times Square, I was always careful to include some middle class characters. I wrote about the collisions—sometimes absurd and sometimes tragic—between the classes.

One other deeply inspiring place was Sally's. It was a transvestite/transsexual bar on 43rd Street near 8th Avenue. After it burned down, Sally, the sometimes-transvestite owner, moved his operations to the Carter Hotel. The majority of the "girls" in Sally's weren't weekend "trannies". They lived full time as females and were in various stages of the transformation. All of them had tits, but a lot of them hadn't cut their dicks off yet. Most of them were professional lip-synchers. They could do Whitney, Barbara, or Sade better than those original singers could do themselves.

There was a fairly heavy chemical trade going on in the place, too. You could buy hormones from Europe along with the crack, dope and weed being sold. Every once in a while, a sex change from Philadelphia who worked for a doctor would come up with a shipment of loose silicone. She'd set up shop on somebody's kitchen table, and the girls would pay her for silicone shots to round out their asses, thighs, cheeks or other body parts. It wasn't the healthiest thing they could do. Loose silicone sends the body into emergency drive. After an injection some of the girls would have to lay up for a day or two until the fever and pain subsided.

I can't say that the girls of Sally's were overly fascinated by me. I wasn't a trannie chaser and I wasn't faggy enough to be one of their "daughters". So why did I keep hanging out there? The answer was simple. I was into the trannies' boyfriends. Transsexuals and transvestites attract the most masculine men that exist. Think about it. Not only do they have to be heterosexual enough to dig a woman, they also have to be macho enough to control a man. The problem was, most of the trannies' boyfriends weren't into somebody like me, who looked too much like a man. There was, however, one notable exception. They called him Izod, after the shirt.

Izod was a light-skinned Puerto Rican with a beautiful pompadour, slightly Asian eyes and massive shoulders. He pretty much had his rhythms down to a science. He'd get a trannie and a john to support him at the same time. With the money he'd develop a major crack habit. Sooner or later, the habit would land him in jail. Then he'd cool out, gain weight and come back on the street.

Crack habit and all, I did everything in my power to get Izod to move in with me. When he finally said yes, I met him at a bar where he left all his bags with me. All he said he needed was forty dollars to pay a dealer in the hotel across the street. Otherwise, they were going to waste his ass. I gave Izod the forty and waited with his bags for him to come back from that hotel. Only problem was, he never did. Once he paid the forty back, the dealer treated him to a few free tokes. Before he knew it, he had smoked enough crack to become the dealer's slave again. I saw him on the corner about three days later. He was dealing, too.

Both Sally, the club owner, and Izod were big inspirations to me. Composites of both appear in my novel *User*.

Well, that's about it for the subject of gay bars and gay writing.

BACKPACKER

Hillary Raphael

Originally Published: 2003

best garments i've ever had on

- a black nylon dress with a steel belt buckle attached
- a pair of fake brand-name sneakers with clear air bubbles in the soles
- a navy blue leather blazer
- a t-shirt with a drawing of a capsule on the front
- grey wool herringbone tights
- a tiny beige sweater with one huge snowflake knitted into it
- a sunshine yellow moto-racing jacket
- a white shearling coat
- a silver velvet dress embossed to look like lizard
- a dark-blue and medium-blue striped bikini
- a white paper hospital gown
- a pair of scuffed leather boots with four strips of

velcro and two zippers
a commando sweater
a fuschia silk scarf covered with french obscenities
a backless leotard

a book a fruit farmer gave me and a crucial
    memory

A Handbook of Ecstasy [18th c.]

*The concept of meditation includes two elements. One
is contemplating a thing, while the other is getting at it
at length. To contemplate something means to grasp its
essence and understand it fully. Contemplation therefore
only pertains to the depth of understanding derived from
itself. At first thought, one may think that contemplation
is the depth of knowledge. This is not true, however, since
the depth of knowledge is only like a vessel with which
one arrives at the depth of a concept.*

*Wisdom is the concept of nothingness in an idea, the state
in which it exists before it comes to the level of points that
can be grasped by understanding. Just as there is depth,
breadth, and length to Understanding, which is called
Somethingness, so there is depth, breadth, and length in
Wisdom, which is called Nothingness.*

*Wisdom consists of a new concept that enters the
mind like a flash of lightning. Its place of origin is its
hidden depth, which is its primary intrinsic nature
and innermost essence. This is the depth of the concept
Understanding, which when understood, is experienced*

*as an aspect of Somethingness. The concept can then be
revealed so that it can be explained.*

Oh, yeah.

I can't leave one thing untold about the times on
the dance-slash-farming collective on the outskirts
of Sapporo that we called the Lavish Future. This is
before Kenzo was killed. Kenzo went with his sisters
to a family funeral, by bullet train, and came back
to the farm the next night. It was the first, last, and
only time I'd ever seen him in a suit. He actually wore
one: light wool of dark charcoal gray, a crisp blinding
white shirt, and flat black tie. He didn't look at all like
a salaryman, but only like a dancer in a formal outfit.
Very exquisite. Stumbling drunk out of a taxi at the
farm's gate, he was weaving his way down the path
towards the Bathing Room. So unbelievably drunk,
he could barely stand. I was slightly scared of him
because I didn't know what to say, so I just watched.
I thought he would tear off his clothes and jump into
the tub, maybe even without washing first. Instead,
he sank to the ground, sitting on the dirt, leaning
against the side of the building. He pulled out his
cigarettes and this metal lighter he had with a huge H
on it. H for Helena, which he used constantly, which
I can't believe Steve never mentioned, as it was his
trademark accessory. Kenzo sat there, smoking quietly, looking up at the sky. There were a lot of stars,
but no moon, and it was chilly. I started to worry he
would catch cold, so I lost my fear of him, and just

imagined him as the little asthmatic bullied kid he once was before I knew him. I decided to bring him in somewhere, but not necessarily to the Sleeping Room because his body suggested not wanting to see other people. My chest was hurting, I felt a mix of so many things watching him, being separate from him, but not because he was on stage or in the field, but because his head was somewhere else. I stomped out into the path, and he saw me. His eyes tracked me through a mosquito netting of drunkenness. I hoped he wouldn't throw up.

'Hey, Kenzo. Welcome home,' I told him in Japanese, even though he often made fun of my accent and said I spoke like a Christian missionary or escort service girl. He stood up, bobbed and weaved further down the path toward where I stood. I tried to smile, but my face felt detached, like a sore muscle numbed by an ice pack. He charged at me, grabbed me by my upper arm, and steered me, not gently, into the Bathing Room. Then, super-gently, he pushed me down to sit on the wooden step next to the tub. The air was damp and warm, as though it were midday inside while it was midnight outside. He carefully folded my legs for me, so that I was sitting cross-legged. I could smell the shochu coming off his skin. He looked at me and nodded. Then Kenzo pulled off his stiff-leather men's shoes and damp thin socks, but left his jacket and tie intact, and lay down in my lap, and he curled his body around me so tight he might have been able to levitate over me— every muscle was engaged, every fiber of his suited body was participating in being wrapped around me and laying in my lap. He cried and cried, wetting my lap for about five minutes, then fell asleep. I backed up a few inches, so I could prop myself against the wall, and I let him sleep. I watched him breathing, dreaming. I stared at him a long time, and I catalogued every hair on his head, his fingernails, his toenails, his slight twitching while he slept, his eyelashes, his knuckles, his belt buckle, a hole that had healed shut on his earlobe. Amazing, I thought, really amazing. At that moment, he darted up, out of my lap, like a sleek missile of male energy.

'Don't stare at me.'

I was too weirded out to answer. The coolness of the air, and the darkness made me just want to cling to him and stare some more, until he'd metabolized all the cheap domestic vodka and would be right again.

'I'm serious, Helena, don't stare at me.'

'I'm not.' I said it softly so he'd realize that I'd stayed up waiting for him to get back. 'How was your cousin's funeral?'

'It was fine. Next time you should come with me, see my village. OK?'

'OK.' I knew I shouldn't make a big deal out of it. We had never discussed life outside the farm together before.

'Helena, I'm serious. I'm not drunk any more.'

'OK, Kenzo. Got it.' I could feel the earth shifting us together, toward real life. I knew I was ready to radically fuse with another creature.

'I want to live there with you. In a small house. But we won't tell anyone until the last minute. They'll be too jealous.'

'Yeah. Too jealous.' I was bathed in happiness. Happiness pulsed through me in sluices of light. I was floating, glowing from within, bobbing in golden breezes. When I looked at him, it was like viewing him from across a sunlit lake.

'Helena, please forgive me for something.'

Confusion. 'What?'

'I went to a love hotel with a funeral person.'

Continuing confusion. 'What?'

'An office lady from my uncle's company.'

'You fucked an OL?' My bowels were loosening swiftly.

'It wasn't the first time. I fucked several older OLs when I was in high school.'

Moodkiller, moodkiller! I couldn't have regretted more waiting up for him. 'Wow, Kenzo, you're a real superstar. What do you want me to do, start crying?'

'No, don't cry. I just want to give you her love note. As proof that I don't love her. I have all of yours in a Milky Cookie tin, with a couple of fruit jellies.'

'Fine, asshole, give it to me.' Kenzo bowed to me, for real, not playing, keeping his head down for ten seconds or even more. I took the folded peach paper. 'Get up, get up, don't grovel, this isn't boy's kendo camp.'

It was written all phonetically. Was this little slut a

retard? I bit my inside lip, tasted blood, then bit more as I read:

dear ken-kun,

i have to open my heart to you, no matter the cost to my pride. when you touched me for the first time, my whole body cried with happiness. your hands, your mouth, your skin are intoxicating—more than alcohol or any drug. your whispers in my ear make me come even if i try to hold back. you are so different from any man i've known.

let me whisper back to you. i need to tell you of my love for you. this will never die. our night together gave me hope to continue in this life. you have battled, and defeated my tendency to despise life and want to end it.

you came from the heavens to enrich my life and fill my heart with passionate goodwill. let me be with you! i need to know that my life has a central meaning—and that is curling up again into the muscles of your arms and lapsing into an orgasmic slumber.

below is my cellular phone number.

i love you, you know.

reiko

Just thinking about what he must've done to her to inspire her to write this drivel made me fantastically jealous. I was tempted to call the number just to tell her that she had better erase whatever masturbatory fantasies she was harboring because he signed them over to me, but I resisted doing that. Let her remember whatever she wants to, I figured, it'll be worse to never relive it.

most satisfying sex binges

piazza duomo, firenze, italy/ male nurse ginza business hotel, tokyo, japan/ female nurse kruger national park tent, south africa/ jeep driver rice farming collective, guilin, china/ farmer residential tower, new york, usa/ consul general of denmark ramon crater, negev desert, israel/ rescue helicopter pilot roman coliseum, el jem, tunisia/ dog sledder las pirámides, lake atitlán, guatemala/ vision quest guide desert suites, las vegas, nevada, usa/ mc donald's cashier hut, tromsø, norway/ interpreter

What can be said to spread ecstasy from one person to another? It's a lost detail, a subtle movement at the center of a million coarse ones. It's a vibrating wave connecting seemingly unrelated instants in thematically-linked compartments. It's stepping onto the metro in a new city and eavesdropping on a conversation about someone you know, and remembering the vague miracle of meeting anyone, ever. Ecstasy is recalling something precious lost and not minding at all.

METRODADDY V. UBERMUMMY

Mark Simpson

Originally Published: 2005

MS: WHAT DO YOU MAKE OF THE REPORTS IN SOME QUARTERS THAT YOUR BABY IS 'DEAD'?

MS: Rumours of his death have been greatly exaggerated. Mostly by the marketing woman who kidnapped him two years ago, who has I believe another book to sell.

MS: SOMEONE SHOULD CALL SOCIAL SERVICES ABOUT THAT WOMAN.

MS: I blame myself. I should have fought harder for custody of the metrosexual. But I worried about him seeing my piles of dirty Y-fronts and I had no place to put his shoe collection.

MS: HE WOULDN'T HAVE UNDERSTOOD HOW METRODADDY COULD LIVE LIKE THAT.

MS: OK, so the world may be—finally!—growing bored with the word 'metrosexual', which apparently I coined back in 1994 but which no one took much notice of until I returned to the subject again for Salon.com in 2002, prompting the last three years of metrosexmania—a media and marketing global gang-bang that makes the rape of Berlin by the Red Army seem like a pre-teen pyjama party. Despite the resulting, ahem, slackness of the word itself, the metrosexualisation of men continues apace. Masculinity is more mediated, more commodified, more exhibitionistic, more self-conscious, and more tarty than ever.

MS: I HAD A NEW FRIDGE DELIVERED YESTERDAY AND THE TWO MACKS CARRYING IT WERE WORKS OF ART. I FELT LIKE A DESPERATE HOUSEWIFE—ONE WHO SPENDS WAY LESS TIME ON HER APPEARANCE THAN THEY DO.

MS: Things have gone so far and so fey that even a retrosexual these days is frequently merely a metrosexual with shaped chest hair—or sporting one of those neatly trimmed, Emperor Hadrian/Guy Ritchie type beards that merely emphasise an exquisite boy-

265

ishness.

MS: YEAH. LOTS OF GAYS HAVE BEEN WEARING THOSE SCRATCHY BEARDS FOR YEARS NOW. IT'S A GREAT WAY OF PUTTING THE CHICKS OFF: 'NO, I CAN'T DATE YOU—IT WOULD RUIN YOUR COMPLEXION'.

MS: David Beckham, the man I once dubbed the 'uber-metrosexual'—sound familiar?—may be somewhat out of fashion at the moment in the UK, but largely that's just because he's been upstaged. Despite their gargantuan salaries, the entire Chelsea FC squad, led by Fabulous Frankie Lampard, seems to be moonlighting as male strippers. Even rugby, once the sport of hairy beer monsters, has gone raving metro with those gym-built-bodies, those oh-so-tight Gaultier-esque strips to show them off, and don't get me started on Gavin Henson's hilarious hairdos. Ditto cricket: the Ashes were won back from Australia this year by the gallant efforts of an England all-rounder hero who likes to wear a diamante ear-stud, a bashful come-hither grin and impeccably-cropped hair.

MS: NEXT TO IAN BOTHAM HE LOOKS LIKE A COMPLETE POOF.

MS: Or rather—an entirely different species. Metrosexual. With all these preening heroes, a whole generation of boys has been metrosexualised. A recent survey of 2000 teen males in the UK found that

266

on average, boys admitted to looking in the mirror ten times a day. 96% of these young narcissists used deodorant, 90% used hair-styling products and 50% moisturisers while 72% would like a makeover. This new-found male self-consciousness comes at a price, however: 62% "disliked" their faces and 25% said they "might have plastic surgery".

MS: BUT WHAT ABOUT THE 'UBERSEXUAL' THAT THE MARKETERS WANT TO REPLACE THE METROSEXUAL WITH? DOESN'T HE SOUND NICE AND SHINY AND NEW-FANGLED?

MS: More like some kind of Nazi memorabilia fetishist. The 'ubersexual' is just a badly repackaged metrosexual. Any discussion in the style pages of the media about what is desirable and attractive in men and what is 'manly' and what isn't, is simply more metrosexualisation, even if it doesn't come, as it has in this case, directly from marketers who have every interest in even more buying and selling of maleness.

MS: WE'RE ALL HUSTLERS NOW, BABY.

MS: Yeah, but not everyone is buying. Contrary to most of the skin-deep coverage of the last two years, metrosexuality is not about going to spas and wearing flip flops, nor is it essentially 'girly' and 'feminine'—

unless you think that narcissism and self-centredness are essentially feminine qualities. Metrosexuality—do I really have to spell it out?—is mediated masculinity. Mediated masculinity that has replaced the 'real' thing. This is why I described the metrosexual as a collector of fantasies about the male sold to him by the media. Those fantasies can be faux butch ones as well as faux fairy ones. Or both.

MS: YOU MEAN LIKE BRAD THE-ABS-THAT-LAUNCHED-A-THOUSAND-SIT-UPS PITT IN *TROY* WHERE HE SEEMED TO PLAY BOTH ACHILLES AND HELEN?

MS: Yes, and was felled by Orlando Bloom's devastating cheekbones. Certainly metrosexuality is not something that is 'replaced' or 'killed off' by even more glossy self-consciousness—from advertising execs. If you look at the list of so-called 'ubersexuals' that the marketers have come up with many of them, such as Brad Pitt, Arnold Schwarzenegger and Bill Clinton were on their list of metrosexuals two years ago. What turned these celebs from metrosexuals into ubersexuals in such a short period of time?

MS: IN THE CASE OF CLINTON, MAYBE IT WAS A QUADRUPLE-BY-PASS OPERATION.

MS: Well, desperation certainly had something to do with it. The demand for something 'new' but safely empty. To repackage. Ubersexuals are metrosexuals with the addition of—even more—media faddishness. The metrosexual is dead! Long live the metrosexual!

MS: WHY DOES THE MEDIA PLAY ALONG WITH THIS? WHY HAVEN'T THEY POINTED OUT THE NEW MONEY FOR OLD-SOAP-ON-A-ROPE DIMENSION?

MS: Because it sells newspapers, which very few things do these days, and because, largely due to their weakness caused by the proliferation of media which helped produce the metrosexual himself, newspapers are now a subdivision of the marketing-PR-repackaging business. Ironically, the only publication I've read that had a critical distance on the ubersexual guff was Advertising Age. The New York Times and all the other 'serious' newspapers just reprinted all this ubertwaddle as if it were the findings of a NASA Mars probe. Except nearer the front.

MS: DIDN'T RUSH LIMBAUGH WHINE ABOUT NOT BEING ON THAT LIST OF UBERSEXUALS?

MS: Yes, but he was probably just excited by the Germanic overtones of the word 'uber'. The reality is that Limbaugh is just a rather uninspiring retrosexual. The kind that reminds you why metrosexuality is so appealing.

MS: THE MARKETERS' CLAIM THAT WHEREAS THE METROSEXUAL WAS 'JUST GAY ENOUGH', THE UBERSEXUAL 'DOESN'T INVITE SPECULATION ABOUT HIS SEXUALITY'? KINDA CREEPY, NO?

MS: This is the only significant difference between the 'ubersexual' and the metrosexual: the ubersexual is much more uptight. That's because he represents the marketer's obsession with trying to straighten out the metrosexual, to rid the him of his seeming queerness and his narcissism—the very things that made him interesting, and glamorous, and gorgeous in the first place. Ironically, the very things that drew the marketers' attention. They tried to do this with the metrosexual when they abducted him from his queer daddy two years ago, insisting, over and over, that he was always straight, OK??, and not so narcissistic, actually, more of a family guy, y'know? I kid you not. This earnest squareness was in contrast to my ambiguous, vainglorious definition: "He might be officially gay, straight or bisexual, but this is utterly immaterial because he has clearly taken himself as his own love-object and pleasure as his sexual preference".

MS: I DEFINITELY KNOW SEVERAL GUYS LIKE THAT. OR AT LEAST, I'D LIKE TO KNOW SEVERAL GUYS LIKE THAT.

MS: Marketers, I'm afraid, have small minds; they

worry what the neighbours will think. They're curtain twitchers. In fact, they're worse than that: they measure curtain twitching. They imagine the way to persuade billions of men to buy more product is to keep telling them there's nothing faggy about being... faggy. Which has a kind of truth to it, but it sort of misses the point that a certain kind of fagginess is exactly what is appealing to many straight men.

MS: TELL ME ABOUT IT. LIKE QUENTIN CRISP, I'VE ALWAYS FOUND OBVIOUSNESS A GREAT ADVERTISING STRATEGY.

MS: Unsurprisingly, the aversion therapy the marketers subjected the metrosexual to didn't work—people insisted on being interested in his ambiguity. So what did they do? In order to metrosexualise those retrosexual men still holding out, buttocks clinched, against moisturiser, they tried to murder the 'metrofag' and put in his place the hyper-het, sexually hygienic, 'ubersexual'. What could be straighter than Donald Trump? That ubersexual list they came up with reads like a straight pride parade. Hilariously though, this great victory for posterboy heterosexuality is the very thing that guarantees that everyone will have forgotten about the ubersexual even more quickly than they'll forget about the metrosexual. The ubersexual is just a late 80s ad campaign for shaving foam. Cue cheesy MOR screecher: 'GILL-ETTE!! THE B-E-E-E-EST A MAN CAN GET!!'

MS: HANG ON, DOESN'T THAT MARKETING WOMAN SAY IN HER BOOK *THE FUTURE OF MEN*, THE ONE THAT GAVE THE WORLD THE UBERSEXUAL, THAT METRODADDY WAS 'OPENLY DERISIVE AND DISMISSIVE OF THE CREATURE HE HAD DISCOVERED'?

MS: Well, I've admitted that I was not the best dad in the world to the metrosexual, even though I gave birth to him, which is, let's face it, more than most fathers do. Yeah, I've been a little harsh on him and his materialism sometimes—perhaps out of jealousy of his good looks and all the attention he got. But 'openly derisive and dismissive' 'from word one' is just untrue. As 'proof' UberMummy uses a quote from an article I wrote eight years after my original one and presents it as taken from the original. It's a bit like finding yourself in a custody battle with a woman who will say anything to make sure you're denied even visitation rights.

MS: WHICH IS REALLY CONFUSING IF YOU CAN'T REMEMBER THE LAST TIME YOU SLEPT WITH A WOMAN.

MS: Like the metrosexual himself, my feelings towards him are complex and ambivalent: he's a product of a mediatised consumerist world but he's also a response to it. But I'll tell you what: since he's been subjected to a homophobic kicking by those who have exploited him so shamelessly over the last couple of years, I've seen a lot more good in him.

MS: SO WHAT DO YOU PREDICT WILL FOLLOW METROSEXUALITY IF NOT UBERSEXUALITY? UNTERSEXUALITY? RURALSEXUALITY?

MS: Sorry to be boring, but barring a nuclear winter, or worse, a strike by personal fitness trainers, just more metrosexuality. Male vanity and mediated self-consciousness is a genie that can't be put back in the Armani bottle. Male sensuality and 'selfishness' is necessary to sustain a global consumerist economy. Men must tint their eyelashes, otherwise we all starve.

MS: PERSONALLY I'D RATHER STARVE THAN HAVE PALE EYELASHES.

MS: Feminism has also made all this masculine self-indulgence indispensable. If men are, as some have put it, being more like 'women' maybe it's because they can't rely on women to be 'women' for them any more. Or even to stick around. Metrosexuality is a stab at a certain type of commodity-supported independence on the part of men. Armed with 'product', they're not quite so dependent on a woman's love, which is often a fickle thing in this day and age, but rather on their self-love, which in men we still tend to see as being sick or queer or laughable. In women, of course, we just call it 'self-reliance'.

MS: YOU GO FOR IT, GURL! BECAUSE YOU DESERVE IT!

MS: Exactly. The double-standard here is remarkable. Can you imagine the furore if a man wrote a book called *The Future of Women*? One in which women were attacked for daring to appropriate characteristics traditionally associated with men to try and get ahead, or just survive? Compared to retrosexuals, metrosexuals, having imbibed the lessons of feminism in utero, don't necessarily need women to dress them, feed them, tell them what they're thinking or feeling—or what their future is. Some women find this a blessed relief. Others, such as UberMummy, seem to find it just another reason why they want him dead.

STRIPPER EXCUSES

Noah Cicero

Originally Published: 2006

Introduction: These are things I've heard strippers say to either not come to work or to leave early.

'My grandmother died.'
'My cousin died.'
'My aunt died.'

This one girl who I think is dead now, went through her whole family in one month.

'I'm bleeding like a stuck pig.'

Think about it.

'I have a yeast infection.'
'I was outside in the cold, and my nipples were hard for a long time. And they hurt real bad.'

'I ran out of painkillers and my knee hurts. I need to go home and take more pain killers.'

'Someone just offered me three hundred dollars to have sex with him, but he needs to do it right now.'

'I drank a bottle of Hennessy on the way to work and I'm really drunk.'

'My kid is sick.'

That is for all jobs though. Every job I've ever worked there was always that one bitch whose kids got sick every fucking week. You would think she was feeding them germs.

'My toe is broke.'
'I'm having a bunion removed.'
'Water in the knee.'
'I'm getting breast implants.'
'I'm having a medical procedure Tuesday morning.'

Strip joint managers know what Tuesday morning is. Tuesday is the only day that the discount abortion clinic operates.

'I'm in jail.'
'Gotta wake up and go to court.'
'I was bailing my boyfriend out of jail.'
'My boyfriend's trial is in the morning.'
'My trial is in the morning.'
'My boyfriend beat me up so bad I look like hell.'

'My weave fell out.'

'The cap on my front tooth fell off.'

'My boyfriend got mad and shaved my head.'

'My boyfriend got mad and burned all my dancer clothes.'

'My car broke.'

Also used at every fucking job.

'I got a DUI and they impounded my car.'

Also used at every job.

'I lost my car.'

'I'm sick.'

'I'm having the baby!'

ABOUT THE AUTHORS
(IN ORDER OF APPEARANCE)

Michael Bracewell is the author of six novels and two works of non-fiction. He has written catalogue essays for many contemporary artists, and is a regular contributor to *Frieze* magazine.

A. Stevens is a former Editor of 3:AM Magazine and works as a writer and journalist. He lives in London and São Paulo with his wife and son.

Andrew Gallix lives in Paris with his wife and son. He teaches at the Sorbonne University, writes fiction and is Editor-in-Chief of 3:AM Magazine.

Tim Parks was born in Manchester in 1954, grew up in London and studied at Cambridge and Harvard. In 1981 he moved to Italy where he has lived ever since. He has written eleven novels including *Europa, Destiny, Rapids* and, most recently, *Cleaver*, as well as three non-fiction accounts of life in northern Italy, a collection of 'narrative' essays, *Adultery and Other Diversions*, and a history of the Medici bank in 15th century Florence, *Medici Money*. He has translated Moravia, Tabucchi, Calvino and Calasso, and lectures on literary translation in Milan. (www. timparks.com)

Utahna Faith lives in New Orleans. Her stories appear in various magazines including *Exquisite Corpse* and *Clean Sheets* and in collections such as *French Quarter Fiction* and the Norton anthology of flash fiction. She is a co-editor for 3:AM Magazine and is editor of *Wild Strawberries*, a journal of flash fiction and prose poetry.
(www.wildstrawberries.org)

279

Richard Marshall is one of the Editors of 3:AM Magazine, a job he got following the magazine's decision to publish this piece on Stewart Home. Marshall is a bereft doppelganger.

Jim Ruland is a veteran of the Navy, a part-time instructor of English, and a creative supervisor at a Los Angeles advertising agency. He is the recipient of numerous awards, including a literature fellowship from the National Endowment for the Arts. He also hosts Vermin on the Mount, an irreverent reading series in the heart of Chinatown, contributes to *The Believer* and *Razorcake Fanzine* and is the author of the short story collection, *Big Lonesome*. (www.lazymick.com)

Alistair Gentry is a writer and artist, or an artist and writer. He was born in Bedfordshire and grew up in Essex and Suffolk. He is the author of the novels *Their Heads Are Anonymous* (1997), *Monkey Boys* (1999) and the forthcoming *Nobody Knows Anybody*. He's been an English Heritage/Arts Council England Artist Fellow, with his video work shown in numerous galleries and at the 2005 Venice Biennale. He is an editor and board member of the fiction site Pulp Net.
(www.pulp.net)

Steve Aylett is the author of *Slaughtermatic*, *Toxicology*, *Atom*, *Shamanspace*, *The Inflatable Volunteer*, *The Crime Studio*, *Bigot Hall*, *Only an Alligator*, *The Velocity Gospel*, *Dummyland*, *Karloff's Circus*, *Fain the Sorcerer*, *And Your Point Is?*, *The Caterer* comic, the *Tao Te Jinx* and *LINT*. (www.steveaylett.com)

Kenji Siratori is a Japanese cyberpunk writer who is currently bombarding the internet with wave upon wave of highly experimental, uncompromising, and intense prose. He has published nine books, one of which, *Blood Electric* (Creation Books), was acclaimed by David Bowie. (www.kenjisiratori.com)

Billy Childish, painter, novelist, poet and musician, is the Renaissance man of British culture. (www.theebillychildish.com)

Mike Watt lives in San Pedro, California, USA. He plays music with The Secondmen and The Stooges. He is the author of *Spiels of a Minuteman* (L'oie de Cravan). (www.hootpage.com)

Sander Hicks is a playwright, journalist, songwriter and activist. Hicks founded Soft Skull Press, Inc. in 1996, was lead singer in White Collar Crime from 1996 to 2003, and started Vox Pop/Drench Kiss Media Corporation in 2003. Vox Pop is a New York City's only union-shop, fair-trade coffeehouse/bookstore. Vox Pop recently published Hicks' new book, *The Big Wedding: 9/11, The Whistle-Blowers, and the Cover-Up*. He lives in Brooklyn with his wife Holley Anderson, and their son, Coleman. (www.sanderhicks.com)

James Sallis has written some two dozen books including twelve novels (six of these in the critically acclaimed Lew Griffin series), three books of musicology, a biography of Chester Himes, and multiple collections of stories, poems and essays, as well as translating Raymond Queneau's novel *Saint Glinglin*. He is a columnist for *The Magazine of Fantasy & Science Fiction* and the *Boston Globe*. (www.grasslimb.com/sallis)

Paul Tickell directed the films *Crush Proof* (1999) and *Christie Malry's Own Double Entry* (2002). He has also directed a number of short films (which include *Zinky Boys Go Underground*, *West End Girls* and *A Few Short Journeys*) and a number of documentaries (which include *Frida Kahlo*, *Punk and the Pistols* and *Matisse in Morocco*). *Tempesta*, starring Rutger Hauer, is currently in post-production.

Guillaume Destot's poems, stories and pictures have been published in a variety of international online and print magazines (*Thee Flat Bike*, *The Prague Literary Review*, *Retort Magazine*, *Ken*Again Magazine*, *Cerebration*...). He lives in Paris.

Todd Colby is the author of *Tremble & Shine* (Soft Skull Press, 2004) and *Riot in the Charm Factory: New and Selected Work* (Soft Skull Press, 2000). He recently published a limited edition graphic novel with the artist David Lantow entitled *Sympathetic Detonations* (Evil Clown Books, 2005). The novel is only available by contacting the author. He lives in Brooklyn, NY with his wife, the artist Elizabeth Zechel.

Jim Martin is a writer, computer nerd, 3:AM Magazine Editor, and the frontman for punk band Johnny Incognito. He lives in Calgary with his wife and kids.

Susannah Breslin is a freelance journalist and the author of short story collection *You're a Bad Man, Aren't You?* (Future Tense Books). She is currently at work on a semi-autobiographical novel, *Porn Happy*, based on her experiences in Porn Valley. Her writings, photographs, and comics have appeared in *Harper's Bazaar*, *Details*, Salon.com, Nerve.com, *The LA Weekly*, and *Variety*, among many other publications. (www.invisiblecowgirl.com)

Charlotte Cooper lives in the East End of London. She's a writerjournalistauthorzinester, an associate editor of *Cheap Date* magazine and boss bitch of The Chubsters, a vicious girl gang. She wrote *Fat and Proud: The Politics of Size* and her first novel, *Cherry*, got busted by Canadian Customs for obscenity. (www.charlottecooper.net)

Tony White is the author of two pulp novellas and two novels, including most recently *Foxy-T* (Faber and Faber, 2003). His short stories have been published in numerous magazines, collections and publications. Tony is literary editor of the *Idler* magazine and edited the *Britpulp!* collection (Sceptre, 1999). With Matt Thorne and Borivoj Radakovic, White recently co-edited a short story collection entitled *Croatian Nights* (Serpent's Tail, 2005) which maps literary networks emerging between the UK, Serbia and Croatia. In 2006 Tony White publishes a new non-fiction work entitled *Another Fool in the Balkans* (Cadogan, 2006). 'Afternoon Play' was written as a sequel of sorts to White's 'The Jet-Set Girls', which was collected in the *Retro Retro* anthology (Serpent's Tail, 2000).

Travis Jeppesen is the author of a novel, *Victims* (Akashic Books, 2003), and a collection of poetry, *Poems I Wrote While Watching TV* (Blatt Books, 2006). He currently divides his time between Prague and Berlin. (www.blatt.cz)

Jeri Cain Rossi is the author of *Angel With a Criminal Kiss* (Creation Books, 1996) and *Red Wine Moan* (Manic D Press, 2000). After a harrowing Huck Finn raft ride through the gale called Katrina, she now resides in San Francisco, California. When asked what she'll do when the Big One hits there, she replied, 'Ah got out 'o one sinkin' city, guess ah can git outta nother.'

Tyondai Braxton lives in Brooklyn, New York, USA. He records as a solo musician and with Battles. He is the author of *Wide* (Slow Toe). (www.tyondai.jmzrecords.com)

Stefano Giovannini's photographs have appeared in many publications. An Italian living in New York, his camera always by his side, Stefano captures the essence of life. (www.stefpix.com)

Thurston Moore lives in Northampton, Massachusetts and plays music with Sonic Youth. He edits the Ecstatic Peace

Poetry Journal. He is the author of *Fuck a Hippy, but be a Punk* (Glass Eye) and *Mix Tape: The Art of Cassette Culture*. (www. ectstaticpeace.com)

Leah Singer is a visual artist and writer. Her fiction has been published in Purple and Soft Skull Press and her journalistic work about the arts has aired on CBC radio.

Lee Ranaldo plays music with Sonic Youth and Text of Light, among others projects. Recent solo recordings include *Music for Stage and Screen* (DSA) and *Oasis of Whispers*, with Glen Hall and William Hooker (Alien8). His most recent book is *Lengths & Breaths* (Water Row Books). (www.sonicyouth.com/dotsonics/lee)

Matthew Wascovich lives in Cleveland, Ohio, USA. He plays music with Thee Scarcity of Tanks and A Real Knife Head. Wascovich runs Slow Toe Publications & Records and edits *Thee Flat Bike* poetry journal. (www.slowtoe.com)

Daren King was born in Harlow, Essex. His debut novel, *Boxy an Star*, was shortlisted for the *Guardian* First Book Award. He has written two other novels for adults, *Tom Boler* and *Jim Giraffe*, and written and illustrated an adult cartoon book, *Smally's Party*.
(www.darenking.co.uk)

Tony O'Neill's debut novel *Digging the Vein* is published in the US and Canada by Contemporary Press, and in the UK by Wrecking Ball Press from Summer 2006. He has previously played with bands and artists including The Brian Jonestown Massacre and Marc Almond. He lives in New York. (www.tonyoneill.net)

Richard Cabut played in the punk rock group Brigandage, produced the fanzine *Kick*, and wrote for the music papers under the pen name Richard North. Now, he contributes to various national magazines and papers, and writes fiction and poetry in London.

HP Tinker lives in Manchester where he has been called the Thomas Pynchon of Chorlton-cum-Hardy. His fiction has appeared in *Ambit*, Pulp.Net, *emwriting*, *CrimeSpree Magazine*, *Dreams That Money Can Buy*, and laurahird.com. Three of his "post-Gibson, neo-Lynch" crime vignettes were anthologised by Nicholas Royle in *Dreams Never End* (Tindal St Press, 2004) and praised by *The Times* for their "hilarious deadpan surrealism." (www.hptinker.co.uk)

Paul Ewen was born and raised in New Zealand and now resides in South London. (www.londonpubreviews.co.uk)

Tom Bradley is a novelist exiled in Nagasaki. The five novels that comprise his Sam Edwine Pentateuch have been nominated for The Editor's Book Award and The New York University Bobst Prize, and one was a finalist in The AWP Award Series in the Novel.
(www.tombradley.org)

Steve Almond is the author of two story collections, *My Life in Heavy Metal* and *The Evil BB Chow*, and the non-fiction book *Candyfreak*. He lives and rocks in Somerville, MA. (www.stevenalmond.com)

Steven Hall's 'Stories for a Phone Book' appears in the British Council's *New Writing 13* anthology. His first novel *The Raw Shark Texts* will be published by Canongate. (www.steven-hall.co.uk)

Ben Myers is a writer and journalist. He has published a number of short stories, poems and music biographies and his first novel *The Book of Fuck* is out now. He lives in London, where he also runs the Captains of Industry record label. (www.benmyers.com)

Bruce Benderson is the first American to win France's prestigious literary prize, the Prix de Flore. He is the author of two books of fiction, *User* and *Pretending to Say No*, and a memoir, *The Romanian* as well as the book-length essay *Towards The New Degeneracy*. He has translated authors including Robbe-Grillet and Nelly Arcan from the French.

Hillary Raphael is the author of the cult classic *I [Heart] Lord Buddha*, and the forthcoming *Backpacker* (both Creation Books). She travels around the world constantly. (www.tokyomonamour.com)

Mark Simpson was born in York, England and attended the same school as Guy Fawkes, though not in the same year. He is a writer and journalist, and has been blamed/credited for inventing the term 'metrosexual'. According to the *Independent on Sunday* he 'writes with enough panache to make most of his peers toss their laptops into the waste disposal and weep.' (www.marksimpson.com)

Noah Cicero has written three books: *The Human War* (Fugue State Press), *The Condemned* (Six Gallery Press) and *Burning Babies*, which is published is forthcoming in 2006. He has been published at *Black Ice*, *Retort Magazine*, *Prague Literary Review*, and *Nth Position*.

ACKNOWLEDGEMENTS

The editor would like to thank Utahna Faith, Andrew Gallix, Richard Marshall, Richard Nash and Matthew Wascovich for their assistance in putting this anthology together and James Bridle at Snowbooks for seeing it through.